Wait Gabriel Wait

Also by Winalee Gentry
One More River To Cross

The amusing true story
of a great-grandmother who proved life
could be fun and kept saying . . .

Wait

Gabriel

Wait

by Winalee Gentry

Foreword by
United States Senator Charles H. Percy

To my mother
who taught me how to live . . .

ISBN #0-914518

Second Printing

Library of Congress Catalog Card Number: 73-92308

Printed in the United States of America

Products Corporation, Unlimited
Waterville, Ohio 43566

I wish to express deep appreciation to my daughter, Winalee Gentry Mitchell, a woman of many talents, for her encouragement when I was writing this book. She served as a constant help to me during the time I was putting the story together. Whenever the task I had set before me seemed overwhelming, it was she who convinced me to continue.

I would also like to thank Sharon Jo Alwart, who, together with my daughter, shared a high standard of perfection in the editing of this book.

Winalee Gentry

Contents

Foreword

What do you do with a mother who comes to live with you and your family and won't let you play cards in your own home, raises chickens in your husband's tool shed, remonstrates your every move and wants to reorganize your household?

If you are my friend, Winalee Gentry, you face the situation as positively and lovingly as you can. In her book, Mrs. Gentry provides us with a witty, albeit realistic, account of incorporating her mother into her full family circle. Maintaining harmony in a three-generation household was not an easy task at first, but soon they came to realize that the situation could be beneficial to all.

Mrs. Gentry explains that initially she tried to teach her mother "how to live," although it soon became apparent that this elderly lady had already learned that lesson herself. Conversely, the Gentry family had no intention of having their lives regulated by someone with the mores of a previous generation. Finally, tired of trying too hard to make the situation work, of being too conciliatory, the family discovered that they couldn't change her. It was only after she felt their support and appreciation that she decided to change herself, and they found their lives could blend together after all.

This story speaks to us on a deeper level as well. The trend in the United States now is toward young people, and our vast elderly population is all but disregarded. The experience of the Gentry family serves to show us that extended family relationships can be warm and supportive; it shows us that the wisdom of the elderly is not lost on our younger generation, and, more important, that the elderly can and want to continue to make a contribution to their families and their society.

It is true that not all great-grandmothers will have the spunk and stamina to attend a six-week course at charm school, nor will all of them want full-time jobs, but it is certain that their lives can have purpose and add meaning to the lives of those of us who are younger. Winalee Gentry's charming story bears out a truth all of us should realize.

Charles H. Percy
United States Senator

1

Beloved Stranger

The crucial moment was almost here, and I wished that Dux, my husband, had come with me. He always seemed to know how to handle sensitive situations.

Since I was a few minutes early, I wandered over to the newsstand and glanced over the papers for the latest war news from Europe. These first few months of 1940 would be long remembered in history. Hitler had just invaded Denmark and Norway, but somehow, on this beautiful spring day, it seemed so far away.

Suddenly I realized the Greyhound Bus had already pulled up onto the ramp and was unloading. Passengers with coats, packages and small bags spilled down the steps.

Then I saw her. Framed in the doorway of the bus, scanning the faces below, stood a short gray-haired lady, hat slightly askew, a cardboard box braced

against her drooping bosom, a large black handbag dangling from one wrist, while under her arms she gripped packages and books. To everyone else, she must have appeared a quaint, old-fashioned woman—too fat, quite plain, even a bit rumpled—but to me she was beautiful, all five feet of her. My mother! My delight in seeing her was overwhelming.

An instant later, however, my misgivings returned, and two perplexing questions raced through my mind. This elderly woman had given up her home in West Liberty, Kentucky and had come to live with us in Michigan. Were we right in urging her to leave her relatives and friends? Would she adjust to a new situation and be happy with us?

With a proprietary air, Mother remained standing

for several minutes on the top step. I knew she was looking for me, but although I waved frantically over the heads of the crowd, she didn't see me. Then, pointedly rejecting the outstretched hand of the bus driver, she started down.

As I pushed through the crowd, I noticed that her blue wool suit showed the strain of age, but the gay red hat, balanced precariously on her naturally curly hair, was obviously new. Standing out like a badge of courage, it somehow brightened my spirits. I remembered with a glow of love how Mother had always said, "When you get down in the dumps, go buy a new hat." She had always loved perky headgear, and Dux called them her "go-to-hell hats." "So long as there are milliners, there's hope for you, Chubby," he told her. Her tolerance of the slightly mocking nickname was a mark of her affection for him.

Halfway down the steps, she shifted her purse to get a better grip on the slipping packages. I held my breath, shuddering at the thought of what might happen. It did! An unruly book slid from her grasp and packages and books tumbled to the ground. By some miracle, she had managed to hang onto the cardboard box, evidently containing something special. But one package popped open, scattering balls of brightly colored crochet cotton in all directions.

Instantly the people around her jumped to help. The driver reached for a yellow ball while a Boy Scout crawled under the bus to retrieve red and blue ones. Other passengers collected her books and packages.

"Never mind, Mrs. Baldwin. We'll get everything for you," someone said, and I realized that people were never strangers to Mother for long. Undoubtedly she would know the life history of every man, woman and child who had traveled with her. She loved people, and wherever my independent Mother went, things happened! She could always be depended upon to

19

create a diversion, one way or the other.

As a child, when I first sensed she was different, it bothered me. Too young to appreciate her rare quality of individuality, I wanted her to conform to the standards of my friends' mothers.

I can still remember the set-to we had over the orange-feathered hat she wore to my Sunday School class party. The minute I saw it, I wailed, "You aren't going to wear that!"

"Why not?" she laughed, setting the outrageous creation on her head and fluffing her hair. "I think it's pretty."

"But, Mother, it's too giddy. You're too old."

"Well, honey, I'm not exactly Whistler's mother," she retorted.

Now as she stood next to the bus, murmuring thanks to the people reloading her arms, a tall, tweedy-looking man stooped to pick up a book.

"Here's your western." He looked amused. "You don't really read these, do you?"

"Oh my, yes indeedy!" Mother's face lit up with a quick smile as she tucked the volume snugly under her arm. "Don't you like westerns?" She went on before the man could answer. "Did you know that Wyatt Earp wasn't really the fast-draw he's made out to be on the radio? No, sir! Why, he didn't even have an ordinary six-gun. He carried a Buntline Special, and when the Clantons went after him at the O. K. Corral, they had their guns out before Earp could clear leather with that long barrel."

I kept tugging at Mother's arm, trying to get her attention, but she went right on telling a few bystanders how law and order were brought to the glorious West through the superb courage and blazing guns of our forefathers. Mother loved an audience. What a great actress she might have been! At times, she could hold her listeners spellbound.

When she finally paused for breath, I stepped in front of her, leaned across the cardboard box and kissed her on the lips.

"Oh, Winalee! There you are." She drew a deep breath. "Well, honey, for better or for worse, I'm here!"

The bus driver slammed the baggage compartment door, looked at us and grinned. "Yeah, lady, you sure are." Carrying her suitcases up to the sidewalk, he set them down with a grunt. "What'd you fill these with—gold bricks?" he asked sarcastically, signaling for a porter.

The elderly man piled the luggage into my car trunk and set the last two boxes on the back seat. "Looks like you come to stay a spell," he said, starting to close the door of the car.

"That's right," Mother agreed with a sigh. "From here on out 'til Gabriel blows his horn."

I tried to smile at the old Kentucky expression, but graveyard talk made me shudder.

"Here you are," Mother said as she handed him a dime.

The man smiled and tipped his cap. "Thankee, ma'am. I shore wish you luck."

"Thank you! Most likely, I'll need it."

Mother placed the cardboard box carefully on the front seat.

"Oh, it's wonderful to see you, Mother," I said, hugging her now that her arms were free. "I'm glad you finally decided to come."

"It was a hard decision to make, but I'm here—lock, stock and barrel. What I didn't sell was sent by freight. Some things I thought you'd want," she said as I helped her into the car. "I've burned my bridges, and I just hope you and Dux won't be sorry you asked an old woman to come live with you."

"Of course, we won't, honey," I said, starting the car. "It's such a satisfaction to have you where we can really look after you. Just this morning at breakfast Ginger was saying what a good time she always had at your house—you were so much fun. That's quite a tribute from a seventeen-year-old granddaughter, I'd say."

"Yes, it is." Mother nodded, but her gravity remained. "Never did I expect to live with any of my children. 'No home is big enough for two families.' But then, I'm not a family now, not anymore." Her voice sounded shaky and she cleared her throat. "When you're alone, time drags. It's supposed to go fast when you're busy, but that's only when you've got someone to share your work. It's so lonesome . . ." She broke off and fumbled in her purse for a handkerchief.

I knew I had to be strong. "Now, Mother, we must be grateful for the years we had with Dad. He was such a cheerful person, he wouldn't want you to grieve. Remember how much you used to laugh together?"

"Yes," she said thoughtfully. "People asked us sometimes why we laughed so much, but we never could explain. Just happy, I reckon. It wasn't only that we loved each other—we were friends, too."

As we stopped for a traffic light, I reached over and laid my hand on her knee. "You'll be happy with us, dear. Just you wait and see."

Mother shook her head slowly. "I hope so, but I want to say one thing right now." She spoke with sudden spirit. "I will never interfere. I've heard how fussy old people turn their children's lives topsy-turvy and make a nuisance of themselves." She paused and took a deep breath. "Just give me a place to stay 'til old Gabriel blows his horn. Most likely it won't be for long. My one prayer is that I'll stay in my right mind and not ever be a burden."

"You'd never be a burden and you're not old. Many wonderful years lie ahead of you, honey, if you'll only stop being morbid. You've said yourself that age is just a state of mind."

The car ahead began to move, and I waited for it to make a left turn. "Mother, I like your red hat. When did you get it?"

"Oh, I bought it at a Christmas sale," she answered curtly and quickly returned to her theme. "Well, we never know what's ahead and I don't really care. When you have to give up the home you've lived in most of your life, there's not much left. A house gets to be like an old friend if you've raised a family in it. I'm thankful the Blairs bought my house because they'll love it, as we did."

"Mother, our home is your home now," I said as gently as I could. "We'll do everything in our power to make you comfortable and contented." Even though I knew we were talking at cross purposes, there was nothing I could do about it.

"It's not the same," she said flatly. "Oh, don't think I don't appreciate what you're doing. I'm grateful, but I reckon you're too young to understand how it is with older people who are left alone." She lifted her glasses and dabbed at her eyes.

"Look, Mother," I said quickly, slowing down for a right turn, "isn't that forsythia lovely—like a burst of yellow sunshine!"

"Oh, Winalee, you should see our lot in the cemetery," she responded. "I worked every morning for a week setting out blue ageratum plants on Dad's grave . . ." Her voice broke and she blew her nose. "When I go, I want you to promise you'll take me back to Kentucky. I want to be buried beside Dad."

Unconsciously my foot pressed the accelerator and the car jumped forward. "Please!" Panic was beginning to build up inside me. I looked blindly at the oncoming traffic with hot, hurting eyes. I'd never seen Mother so downhearted. What had happened to her perspective? There had been misfortunes before, plenty of them, but she'd always bounced back with the resiliency of a rubber ball. She was right. I couldn't understand. It's a strange feeling to have someone you've known all your life become alien, with every line of communication broken.

I took a quick look at the stranger sitting next to me. She was staring through the windshield with a forlorn expression on her face. I felt a nostalgic longing for the cheerful, courageous woman who had once been my mother.

2

Lost Independence

Driving along Michigan Avenue, I recalled with hurting compassion the hardships Mother had experienced since Dad's death the year before. I remembered her fierce pride and her pathetic attempts to maintain both her home and her cherished independence. An individualist in her own right, Mother was never one to be dependent on anybody.

After the funeral, dry-eyed and determined, she put her shoulder to the wheel and went to work. There wasn't much money, but the red brick house was free of debt. Dux wanted her to sell it, invest the money and come to live with us, but she wouldn't. Instead, she put out a "Tourists" sign for overnight guests. The venture should have been profitable since the detour for a new highway between Kentucky and West Virginia ran through West Liberty, but it proved to be a losing battle from the start.

"Chubby, it's no use," Dux told her on one of our visits. "You're killing yourself for nothing. The maintenance is eating up your profit, and your generosity isn't conducive to good business. You'd be smart to sell out."

Stubbornly, Mother shook her head. "I will not give up my home. I don't mind the work. Besides, it takes time to build up a trade."

The trade didn't build up, but the problems did—mainly petty, and not so petty, thefts. Many times she would miss towels, washcloths and other small things; once even a wool blanket disappeared. But her faith in mankind was really shattered when a couple made off with all of the family silver. "What I hated most was losing Great-Aunt Liza's Sheffield coffeepot," she had said despondently. "I've always loved it, and I wanted you to have it when I'm gone. I know there's no use crying over spilt milk, but I can't help it. My eyes get wet every time I think of Aunt Liza's pot in thieving hands."

Later when we called her long distance, she informed us that the local piano teacher had quit, and she'd started giving piano lessons again. She already had eight pupils.

"Mother, you can't live on that," I argued. "A dollar a lesson, when children come only once a week, isn't enough for you." But as usual, she was adamant.

"Teaching children is hard work at her age and takes infinite patience," I told Dux. "I wish she'd accept our invitation to come live with us."

"Stop worrying. Chubby'll be all right. I'd rather have her teach children than clean up after tourists," he said. "After all, she's got a lot of spunk!"

True enough, but Dux didn't fool me. He was worried, too, even if he wouldn't admit it. Yet, short of kidnapping her, I didn't know of any way to make her change her mind and come to Michigan.

Then, one morning in March, we were at the breakfast table when the doorbell rang. Dux had his nose in the *Detroit Free Press*, and Ginger, the last of our brood at home, was munching toast while she reviewed her English homework, the notebook propped against the milk pitcher.

"I'll get it," she said, jumping up, and her book slid to the floor. Dux reached for it, but he wasn't fast enough. Probably one of the boys to walk her to school, I thought, and felt a glow of pride in the popularity of our youngest child. Both Lee and Bud, my other children, were married, and Russ, my baby brother, whom Mother had late in life and I had raised, worked on one of Dux's pipelines.

"A special delivery letter from Mam-ma," Ginger announced as she handed it to me. I felt pangs of anxiety as I tore open the envelope.

Dux emerged from his newspaper. "Read it out loud," he said.

> "I've been doing a lot of thinking. School is almost out, and children won't be taking music lessons during vacation, so I can't count on teaching. As you know, Letha Nell Blair's father has been after me for months to sell the house to him, so I finally took the bull by the horns and we closed the deal last night. He bought the carpets, rugs, curtains and a lot of the furniture. Your Aunt Nancy is helping me pack and clean up the place. So I'm accepting your invitation, and I'll be coming to Jackson in a month or

27

so. You are all sweet to want me.
I don't have anything to live for
now, and I'm just waiting for
Gabriel to blow his horn. I hope I
won't be in the way for the little
time I have left."

I choked and wiped my eyes with a napkin.

"Don't worry, Shortie," Dux said as he reached
over and squeezed my hand. "If I know Chubby, she'll
snap right out of this. Her character and temperament
will see her through, but it may take a little time."

But now, turning onto Higby Street, I wondered if
Dux had realized the extent of our problem. Yet the
thought of him lifted my spirits. He'd know how to
handle any situation, and Mother would listen to him.

"Mother, Dux promised to leave the office early
today. He's probably home now, waiting for us. He's
so anxious to see you."

"Dux is a grand man, Winalee." Warmth crept
into her voice. "If I had looked the world over, I
couldn't have found a better husband for you."
Abruptly turning the conversation toward my brother,
Drexel, she said, "Drexel wrote from Alaska that he
had a promotion. They all seem to love Anchorage,
but it's awful to have a son and his family so far
away."

A wave of compassion swept over me. "Maybe
next year you can fly up there to see them."

"Not likely," Mother said mournfully, "and you
know how I feel about flying. Anyway, now that none
of you need me . . ."

"Oh, for Pete's sake, Mother!" My impatience
with her almost caused me to run a stop sign. "Why
do you persist in talking this way? Is there something
you haven't told me? Are you ill?"

"No. Leastways, not that I know of," she said flatly. "I just believe in facing facts and you don't. Even when you were little, you always saw things through rose-colored glasses." She rolled a moist handkerchief into a ball and stuffed it into her purse. "But I'll keep still, no matter how I feel," she snapped. "Now tell me about the family."

"Everyone is fine," I said, feeling like a child who has been given a lollipop to keep his mind off a vaccination. What more could I say? Really, it didn't matter what I said. I might persuade Mother not to talk about old age and death, but I had no control over her thoughts.

We talked of family affairs, and she chuckled about her great-grandchild, my little grandson, Jimmy.

"Is he walking yet?" she asked.

"Oh yes, he's walking. His chubby legs are a bit wobbly, but he manages to get around and into everything." I rattled on, glad to find a subject that would finally bring a smile to Mother's face.

"I wish I could live to see him grow up," she broke in. "Old Man Time and I aren't exactly on speaking terms, galloping along the way he does."

"Now, you listen to me!" I said with a firmness I didn't feel. "You're not really old. You have years ahead, if you don't talk yourself into an early grave. We'll do everything we can to help you make a new life. We'll teach you how to live, but you've got to cooperate."

We drove in silence for a few blocks. I wondered about the vast job ahead. It was going to take a lot of understanding to prop her up and infinite patience and fortitude to disprove that old saying: "No house is big enough for two families."

3

Permanent House Guest

When we rolled to a stop in our driveway, I gave the horn a slight toot. Dux and Ginger came running out of the house, their faces bright with welcome. Then came Martha, our cook, and Ozzie, her brother, to greet Mother and help with the luggage.

"Good to see you, Chubby!" Dux helped her from the car, then swept her up in a bear hug.

"Hi, Mam-ma! We thought you would never get here." Ginger gave her a tight squeeze and leaned down to kiss her cheek.

Mother stepped away from her and beamed. "Let me look at you, honey. You're getting prettier every day."

Then she turned to Martha and took her outstretched hand. "How are you, Martha? I brought that recipe for chess pie I promised you on my last visit."

She looked at Ozzie, pretending surprise. "You still here, Oswald? What devilment are you up to now to worry your sainted sister?" But her smile took the sting from her words.

"Ain't in no devilment this time, Miz Baldwin," Ozzie drawled with a wide grin. "I done got religion."

Martha was our jewel. She had been with us so long she seemed a part of the family, an important part, too, leaving me free to go with Dux on business trips, help with his geological reports, and do a hundred and one things he hated to do himself or didn't want to leave to the girls in the office. At least, that was how I mentally justified hanging onto Martha during times when the budget was strained, almost to an empty cooky jar.

When Martha's scamp of a brother emerged from a series of escapades a couple of years ago, she asked if he could stay with us. Ozzie did odd jobs around the house, kept the grass cut in summer and shoveled snow in winter.

Ozzie had piled the small steamer trunk, suitcases and bundles on the driveway and was reaching for the square box on the front seat when Mother stopped him.

"No, no! I'll take that one. I held it all the way from Kentucky." She placed the box carefully in Martha's hands. "Let me show you," she offered, untying the knot in the string.

We crowded around curiously and gasped when she lifted the lid. The box contained a beautiful cake, frosted in white with pink rosebuds around the edges; across the top in deeper pink icing were the words, "Happy Landing, Hattie."

"Nancy gave a farewell party for me," Mother explained. "When I saw this cake in the center of the table, the tears came. 'Oh, if only Winalee could see it,' I said, and Nancy insisted I bring it to you. She didn't need it for the party. They made over a hundred little cupcakes, and each one had 'Hattie' written on top. Wasn't that wonderful?" she said proudly.

Yes, I thought, it was wonderful, but not unexpected of the good people of West Liberty. A nostalgic wave of gratitude for the Kentucky town where I grew up swept over me. There friendship is more than a word; it's a way of life. How could we have had the audacity to take Mother away?

As we went through the kitchen, Mother sniffed. "My, that does smell good! Martha, you always could cook chicken better than anybody."

"And we got your favorite buttermilk biscuits, cream gravy, black-eyed peas, sorghum m'lasses and pecan pie, too," she said, checking them off on her fingers. "We're livin' high on the hog for you, Miz Baldwin. I'll put that pretty cake in the freezer, and come Sunday, we'll have it when the family gets here."

When we were seated in the living room after dinner, Dux said, "Chubby, we're glad you're going to be with us. You did the smart thing in selling. Those bonds I suggested will bring in a tidy interest check, and with no bills to pay, you can do as you please. Of course," he added, "I know what it must have meant to give up your home, but if you give us a chance, I believe we can make you happy here."

Mother smiled without answering. I knew she thought we couldn't possibly understand what giving up her home had meant, but she was willing to make the best of what she had to do. And I was thinking—she has no idea what a wonderful life is in store for her: a loving family, no cares, nothing to do and plenty of time to do it in. What a reward, after years of work and worry—a utopian existence many older people would envy!

Mother's voice quickly brought me back to the present. "Winalee tells me you're going to teach me how to live," she was saying to Dux, a deceptive mildness in her voice. "I wonder what I've been doing all these years. I thought I was living." She looked first at him, then at me, and waited.

I gulped and glanced at Dux. He looked innocent—a thing he can do to perfection when he wants to convey a lack of knowledge. I wished devoutly I hadn't used those exact words. Somehow they didn't sound the way I meant them, but I knew the damage was done. I hoped the tense moment would pass, but before it did, Ginger unwittingly put my neck right in a noose.

"Mom has rounded up a group of ladies about your age and planned a lot of parties and things. We all want you to have fun."

"You don't say!" Mother gave me the look she always reserved for putting people in their places. "Well, now, let's get some things straight: I do appreciate a place to stay, but I don't want to meet ladies, and I'm through with fun. I know you mean well, but I just want a corner where I can be left alone. I'm satisfied with my life, what there is left of it."

The rebuke was well deserved, and I could feel my face burn. Whatever possessed me to try to manage Mother? At least, I should have been more subtle. I looked at Dux for moral support, but he shook his head and grinned.

"Why don't you take Chubby up to her room, Shortie?" he suggested. "She's probably tired."

"I'm not tired, but I'd feel better after getting unpacked and settled." Mother's voice sounded artificially bright and casual as she started to gather up her things.

"Of course." I jumped up quickly. "I'll help you unpack."

We went upstairs to what had been the guest room. Mother stopped in the doorway, and her eyes traveled over the new frilly organdy curtains, the colorful slipcover on the rocker by the window, the small table with its brand new radio and the bed with the crocheted popcorn-stitch spread she'd given me years before. "You did all this for me?" she asked, walking over to the bed and running her hands over it. "I started this counterpane before Russell was born, remember?"

I nodded. "It's my most prized possession. Guests always remark about it and say they've never seen a more beautiful bedspread."

"No, and they never will, I reckon. There are over a thousand little popcorns. Dad teased me about it and said it would take all my life to finish it." A smile twitched the corners of her mouth. "To tell the truth, this started out to be a spread for Russell's crib until I realized it would be too heavy for a baby. We laughed about it, but I kept crocheting."

My mind flew back to the time when Mother and I had our babies together, her last and my first. Dux and I were living in the oil fields near Tomkinsville, Kentucky where he was drilling wells for the Louisville Gas Company. For some reason, Mother felt sure I'd have a girl, but she was equally certain that she would have a boy. She crocheted and knitted two of everything—one in pink and one in blue. It was such fun getting her packages.

Our sons were born six weeks apart, Mother's baby arriving first. Naturally, Russell Baldwin was the pride and joy of his doting parents, as most late-in-life babies are. But Mother didn't come through the delivery as easily as I did; something went wrong, and she became paralyzed.

We drove to West Liberty as soon as I could

travel. It was a shock to see Mother on crutches. Although she smiled cheerfully at the friends who dropped in to see our babies, her face looked wan and thin.

Help was hard to get, and we finally persuaded my parents to let us take Russ, little dreaming that it would be years before Mother was able to cope with a growing boy.

For Dux and me, it was like having twins, but I felt guilty when I thought of Mother being denied the joy of caring for her baby.

Mother's voice interrupted my train of thought. "Russell must have been eight or nine when this spread was finally finished. By that time, I was busy with music. Now, that's gone. Reckon there's not much left I can do now, and besides, no one needs me any more.

I threw my arms around her. "Oh, Mother, we all need you, but I do especially. There are so many things you can teach me, to crochet for one thing."

"Really?" She brightened. "I've always wanted you to learn, and you could make such pretty things."

For once, I was glad to have said the right thing! If it would make her happy, I'd learn to wield a crochet hook; I'd even let her teach me to stitch quilt squares, a thing we had quarreled about in my girlhood. I hated any kind of handwork, but Mother needed to be needed. Why hadn't I thought of that before?

"Tomorrow I'll put up my family pictures," Mother said. "They'll help make this room more homey. It's such a pretty room, but . . . oh, you don't know how I miss my own home."

"Let's get you unpacked," I said quickly, lifting a suitcase onto the luggage rack and undoing the straps. I started hanging her dresses in the closet while she sat down to take off her shoes. Suddenly she stopped and began to fiddle with the radio knobs.

"I wonder what stations my programs are on. Could you get me a paper with the radio listings? I'll need a clock, too," she said, taking off her wristwatch.

I went to our bedroom and took the electric clock from the dresser. When I plugged it in and set it on her table, I told her I'd go down and get tonight's paper. I thought of what Dux had said before she came: "All Chubby needs is a crochet needle, a rocker and a radio, and she'll be content. How she can listen to those sob stories day after day is beyond me." But for once, I thanked heaven for the soap operas. The radio gave Mother at least one interest!

4

Making Memories

The bright loveliness of the first Sunday morning in May had its effect on me. Full of anticipation, I hurried to Mother's room and knocked on the door.

"We'll be making happy memories today. The whole family will be here," I said.

"Well, I hope I won't be a wet blanket."

I plunged into my "cheerful" routine. "Now Mother, you've always said that when families get together, they're making memories, and I know you don't want to let us down. We'll have dinner about one." I told her Russ had come in late last night, that Bud and Ruthmary would be here in time to go to church with us, and that Lee, Jim and little Jimmy were planning to get in from Flint around noon.

Mother was standing in front of her dresser cramming herself into what looked to me like a cast iron corset, a contraption which caused her to stand very straight, forcing her shoulders back almost like a wooden soldier. Her face was stern and determined.

"I'm not going to church," she said firmly, with a little guilt showing. "I didn't sleep well last night. My bones ache, and if the children weren't coming, I'd stay in bed." She picked up her hairbrush and turned her back on me.

Watching her strained face in the mirror, my thoughts raced back to the mother she used to be. She had always been so enthusiastic, working earnestly for church and community activities and eagerly showing an interest in those around her.

Now she smoothed back her gray wavy hair and tightened her mouth as she said, "Don't worry about me. I won't spoil your day."

Suddenly I knew I would do everything in my power to make things wonderful for Mother—to make these golden years the happiest, or at least the most carefree, of her whole life.   She'd have affection, security and no responsibilities.   After all those years of working, she would now have nothing to do but relax and enjoy herself.   If she wanted breakfast in bed, then she would have breakfast in bed.   How many times had I wished for just one day with nothing to do!

I put my arms around her.   "Oh, Mother, I honestly do believe that when you're adjusted to this change in your life, you'll be happy.   You deserve a good long rest."   Her body stiffened under my touch. Had I said the wrong thing again?

"Come on.   Breakfast is ready, and Dux is waiting. You'll feel better after you eat."   Coaxing her, I took her hand and led her down the steps.

When Dux saw Mother come into the room, he jumped up and pulled out her chair.   "Good morning, Chubby.   It's going to be fun to have the kids with us today.   I'm sure they're anxious to see you."

Mother smiled at him, but said nothing.

She was eating her second piece of coffee cake when we heard Russ and Ginger running downstairs. Mother got up from the table and Russ grabbed her, starting to dance her around the room as if she were his youngest and prettiest girl friend.   Handsome and debonair, he looked like a youthful edition of Dad as he bent down, laughing at his diminutive mother.   She immediately responded to his charm, and I realized how much his attention meant to her.   Their relationship had always been strained, partly because he had lived with us most of his life and partly because of the vast difference in their ages.

Suddenly Ginger grabbed Dux, and said, "Come on, Dad, let's you and I get in on the fun."

He grinned, winked at me and swung Ginger around the table.

As I watched them dance and bump into each other, giggling like children, I thought that it was no wonder our friends often called us the "Crazy Gentrys." But watching Mother's happy face and sparkling eyes made me thankful.

Just then, I heard Bud's knock. He never used the doorbell, but always pounded, like a small boy, in a familiar rhythm. I hurried to open the door.

"Greetings!" Bud, with his arm around Ruthmary, leaned over and kissed me. He was wearing the typically proud and happy smile of prospective parenthood. "Haven't I got the cutest little mother-to-be?"

Ruthmary blushed. "Everyone doesn't think like you do, Howard."

I put my arms around her. "Well, I do, honey. You really look wonderful. You two go on into the dining room and say hello to Mother. We've almost finished breakfast."

We had been home from church only a short time when I heard a car pull into our driveway. I hurried to greet Lee, Jim and little Jimmy.

"Hi, kids!" I caught my grandson as he ran toward me. "How's my little pride and joy?" But he broke away from me when he saw his Daddy Dux.

"Hello, Mother!" Lee kissed me. "Jimmy is so full of vim and vigor, there's no holding him back."

"It's good to see you, Mom," Jim said as he hugged me. "We're earlier than we expected to be. Lee could hardly wait to get here."

"Everyone's in the living room. I'll be with you in a few minutes," I told them and hurried to the kitchen to check with Martha on dinner—a dinner that ran the gamut of delectable southern food from baked country ham and sweet potatoes to her special corn bread.

Throughout the meal, Mother kept us entertained with her old family stories and the children loved it. When it was time for dessert, Martha brought in the "Happy Landing" cake, and little Jimmy shrieked with joy at the sight of the lighted candles. We gave Mother the honor of cutting it, and with great pride, she carefully divided it so as to have a pink rosebud on each piece.

It was thrilling to have us all together again and the day was perfect. True to her word, Mother was by no means a wet blanket. Indeed, she turned out to be the life of the party. For the first time since she'd been with us, she acted more like her old self, like I'd always remembered her to be—happy, carefree and enthusiastic.

5

Storm Signals

During the following weeks, Mother spent most of her time sitting by the window in her rocker, reading her western novels or listening to the radio while her nimble fingers worked back and forth. It seemed to me there was an expression of patience and fortitude on her face and a do-or-die glint in her eyes. Only at mealtime did she seem relaxed and satisfied, eating every bite on her plate and often going back for more.

One morning, armed with determination and courage, I faced the crochet hook. It wasn't Mother's fault that I fell by the wayside. Her casual speed made my efforts seem ridiculously slow and awkward. When I did hurry, I made mistakes. Her "Haste makes waste," "Rome wasn't built in a day," and "Practice makes perfect" didn't help either. It was hard to sit still, and I kept thinking of a hundred and one other things I should be doing.

"Never mind, dear," Mother said finally, waving away my apology. "You're not ready to learn. It's when the years slow you down that you find solace in working with your hands."

Mother crocheted constantly. She'd started white lace "rounds" that were starched and stretched to put under our dinner plates, a smaller size for the cups and saucers and tiny ones for the goblets. "These place mats will save ironing linen," she told Martha. I had to admit they did look pretty on the polished surface of the mahogany table.

Flushed with success, she announced that she was going to crochet antimacassars for the arms and backs of our living room chairs, not seeming to realize that such things went out of style with President Wilson.

Occasionally she would stay downstairs after dinner to chat with Dux or ask Ginger about school activities, but not for long.

If friends dropped in, she'd hurry upstairs at the first sound of the doorbell. "I've got other things to do than visit," she would explain. "I'm busy."

"But you don't have to crochet all the time," I said. "You've already made four place settings and the antimacassars can wait."

"I have to work on my Christmas presents. You can't start too early when you make your own." To Mother, anything worthwhile must be handmade. I'd often heard her say that it was the love and thought which went into a gift that counted.

"Mother, I don't understand you. Since when have you avoided meeting strangers? And these people you'll really like. They're our friends."

"That's just it," she said defiantly. "They're your friends. I'm not going to intrude." Emphatically she added, "Anyway, I don't belong in your age group."

"There's no age group in friendship," I argued.

"Everyone knows you're here, and if you keep hiding, they'll think something is wrong. We're proud of you, and we want to show you off."

She smiled, but shook her head.

I threw up my hands in defeat. "If you insist on hibernating, that's your privilege, but you're missing so much. You need some social life. You've known our neighbors for years, yet you refused an invitation to the Garden Club and wouldn't go to the Tuesday Morning Musicale. How come?"

"Because I'm stubborn, I reckon," she said as she left the room, adding, "I meant it when I said I wouldn't interfere in your life."

That was a laugh! To me, it seemed like that was all she ever did! Mostly her interferences were little things, bones of contention between us, but they had the effect of making me feel petty and foolishly inadequate.

"It's Mother's infuriating rightness that gets me down," I wailed to Dux after one particularly grueling day when everything went wrong. "If only once I could say, 'I told you so.'"

Not that Mother ever said those exact words, but she looked them! And casually she would remark, "Old Man Hindsight is a pretty good teacher, isn't he?"

Mother must have wondered how I had ever managed before she came to live with us. The way she did things was the only way to do them, or so she thought.

The most difficult interference for me to take was in the financial department. She kept telling me how to cut corners, saying I was most extravagant. "Waste not, want not," she quoted when I found her sewing up the tea bags after she'd cut each one in half.

"Most people don't like strong tea, and I think

someone should tell Mr. Lipton. There's enough tea in one of these little bags to make five cups," she declared. "But, of course, Mr. Lipton wants to sell his tea. He isn't interested in saving us money."

She would sail into the kitchen about the time Martha was ready to serve dinner and cut the meat into smaller pieces. "We can take seconds if we want more," she would explain. "This way, it won't be left on our plates, and we'll have enough for another meal. Besides, food is better eaten than thrown away."

Often she would take butter from the refrigerator and put it in the cupboard. "Martha should know that soft butter goes twice as far as hard butter."

Just as often, we would replace it in the refrigerator without saying anything. Finding it there once, she looked suspiciously at Martha, then at me. When Ozzie chose that moment to come through the back door, she snapped at him. "What are you sneaking around for?" The nonplused expression on his face reminded me of a puppy that's been spanked without knowing why.

I laughed. "Don't blame Ozzie, Mother. Maybe we've got little gremlins in the house."

But it wasn't a laughing matter when Mother cut my dinner size paper napkins in half. One of Dux's pet peeves, silly as it seemed to me, was his intolerance of small paper napkins, so I had purchased a whole gross of large ones wholesale. Mother laboriously bisected every one of them!

"Waste is sinful," she scolded. "You ought to be helping Dux in his new venture. 'A penny saved is a penny earned.'"

Dux had recently incorporated his own business and named it the H. L. Gentry Construction Company. We were still in the struggling stages, putting most of our profits back into the business and paying for Dux's new plane, but the future looked bright and we had high hopes.

"Oh, for heaven's sake!" I exploded. "If a few pennies a week are going to break us, we might as well quit right now. Besides, Dux is the one who is earning the money, and if he wants to waste it on large napkins, that's his prerogative."

Mother meant well, I knew. She always meant well, but I was so tired of platitudes, so weary of her soft, beguiling words, "I'd do it this way, if I were you," or "I don't mean to criticize, dear, but . . ." I wasn't a child to be told what to do and how to do it. At times I wanted to scream at her, but she'd look at me in such an appealing way that I instantly felt ashamed. Mother could always say more with looks than most people could with words.

"Don't let it get you down, Shortie," Dux consoled me that night as we were getting into bed. "You're doing a swell job, but remember, honey, it's hard on Chubby, too." He held me close, and in the security of his arms, things seemed less bleak. I was hungry for sympathy and reassurance, but I also wanted to be fair.

"Yes, I know," I said. "I realize it isn't easy for Mother. She misses Dad so much."

He kissed me. "We need to be understanding with Chubby. We need to make her feel that our home is her home also."

Dux was right, as always, and I promised myself to try harder.

6

The Great Compromise

Dux really loved Mother—that was why he was so understanding with her—but I sensed that he was extra tender because he'd lost his own mother the year before. I know he felt guilty that we hadn't made more of an effort to visit Mother Gentry even though we'd received letter after letter begging us to come to New York. We had really intended to go, but before we did, she died unexpectedly of a heart attack.

I could appreciate Dux's compassion for Mother, but it was easier for him because he wasn't with her all the time. Maybe it was my fault that Mother and I got on each other's nerves. I would resolve to be more patient, but then I'd remember the paper napkins and start being irritated all over again. If only she'd be content to let well enough alone, to stop thinking that her way of doing things was best.

I kept telling Dux my side of the story, hoping for sympathy, until he finally got fed up with my constant complaining and decided to become involved.

"Chubby is desperately trying to make the best of it in a home where someone else is boss," he told me thoughtfully. "Put yourself in her place. For the first time in her life, she is playing second fiddle. She's torn between wanting to help and the fear of being told that she's interfering."

"But Dux . . ." I began, feeling I had to defend myself.

He held up his hand. "Wait, let me finish. I've got an idea. We haven't really included her in things—that's why she's been keeping to herself."

"Now, you wait a minute!" I shook my finger at him for emphasis. "I've tried and tried to encourage Mother to do things, to go places, to come downstairs to meet our friends. She won't be included. I'm beginning to think she's anti-social."

Dux laughed as if I'd said something funny.

"Anti-social? Chubby? If I ever saw a gregarious person, it's my bubbly little mother-in-law. She's a remarkable woman who sincerely likes people. All she has to do is smile, and everyone swarms around her."

Yes, that was true. I thought of the small mob at the bus station. No one but Mother could have attracted so many eager beavers on such short notice.

"Yes, Dux, Mother's like that with strangers, but not with her family—at least not anymore. Why doesn't she exert some of her charm on us? All I ever hear about is her loneliness, the 'woeful want' just around the corner and that old horn of Gabriel." I stopped to take a breath and blink back the tears.

Dux put his cheek against mine. "Look, my sweet, I know it's been hard on you," he said softly, "but you and I are adults. We should be able to face our problems realistically, without involvement, right?"

I nodded, fighting the impulse to say that I didn't always feel like an adult. Mother often made me feel like a child again, with a child's lack of experience, a child's awkwardness.

"The trouble with us, honey, is that we've wanted to 'mother' Chubby, to take care of her and force her into a life of ease. I'm beginning to realize that's the wrong approach." He stopped for a moment, lost in thought.

I waited expectantly. Dux always had a flair for pulling order out of chaos. My spirits began to lift with confidence in his ability to find a satisfactory solution.

"It seems to me that we should compromise . . ." he began.

"Oh, for Pete's sake," I broke in, disappointed. "Mother's never been one to compromise. In her book, 'black is black, and white is white and . . .'"

"Compromise is the oil that lubricates all human relationships. It's an essential part of any business," Dux went on, enjoying the sound of his words. "That's what we need here. In the interest of peace and happiness for everyone, we've got to change our tactics."

He put his hand under my chin and kissed me. "We'll give Chubby work to do, really make her feel needed, but let her do things her way, with no comment. It won't hurt us to give in, and once she gets adjusted, she'll be her old cheerful self. Anyway, it's worth a try!"

So I bought his idea, pig-in-a-poke though I thought it to be, but well worth trying if it got Mother out of the doldrums. Both Ginger and Martha approved our "Mother knows best" program, and we all gritted our teeth and went to work.

Theoretically it looked simple, but in practice, as so often happens, the noble experiment, though carried out with love and the best of intentions, backfired!

Almost before we realized what was happening, Mother had taken over and our lives were not our own. Everything in the house revolved around her. She had the decision and weight of an avalanche and was about as easily controlled.

Breakfast at seven, Mother decreed. Always an early riser, she insisted that people who slept late missed the best part of the day. If it was an effort for Martha to start work a full hour earlier, she didn't complain. Ginger, however, did grumble, so Mother agreed to let her sleep late on Saturdays and until time to dress for church on Sundays. This was our one departure from the rigid schedule.

Dinner was served promptly at six. Summer was a busy season for Dux, and he often had to go back to his office afterward, but much to my surprise, he always appeared Johnny-on-the-spot before Martha took the biscuits from the oven.

"Dad never kept me waiting," Mother declared approvingly one evening at dinner. "He was always on time, as any considerate husband would be."

To drive her point home, she told about George and Minnie Cecil back in Kentucky. George fell into such irregular habits after his retirement that Minnie threatened to leave him. He never got to his meals on time. The hired girls wouldn't stand for it, so there was poor Minnie, who wasn't young and wasn't well, standing over a hot stove trying to keep food warm for the inconsiderate brute. "She wasn't retired," Mother pointed out. "A wife never is."

"Well, what happened?" Dux asked.

"Oh, one day Minnie just up and died," Mother answered casually. "She never did learn how to handle a husband. She should have used 'molasses.'"

"Molasses?" Dux looked puzzled.

Mother nodded. "You know—'you can catch more flies with molasses than you can with vinegar.'"

I smiled to myself at the confused expression on Dux's face and changed the subject.

"Did you know that Hitler invaded Paris today?" I asked.

"I heard it over the radio on my way home. I'm afraid the French can't hold out much longer," Dux replied, slowly taking a bite of meat. "That guy Hitler is power crazy—he won't be happy until he takes over all of Europe."

Mother was constantly reminding us not to eat so fast, and Dux was her prime target. She told him she knew a man who died from gall bladder trouble, all because he bolted down his food. So we tried to sit an extra half hour at the table, forcing conversation while leisurely eating our daily bread.

Mother made no specific demands. If she had, I'm fairly sure Dux would have balked, despite the fact that this crusade was his idea.

Martha was giving her all. She concentrated on foods that Mother liked best, and allowed herself to be "taught" how to prepare many of them.

"Miz Baldwin likes hog jowl, I think. Can't we have Mr. Bennet at Henry's to fix us some?" Martha asked. "Poke, too, and maybe we could have some fried grits like they do in Kentucky." She looked at me and grinned.

If there is one thing that Dux and I hate worse than hog jowl, it's poke, a bitter weed that grows wild and isn't fit for man or beast. I was sure Mother didn't like it either. But I was grateful for Martha's help and told her I'd see about calling Mr. Bennet.

Ozzie, surprisingly, was keeping his halo on straight. Mother gave him a Bible with his name on it, and he went to church every Sunday with Martha, even singing in the choir. The strange sounds breaking the stillness of our domain were nothing more ominous than Ozzie's squeaky rendition of "Bringing in the Sheaves" while he worked.

"Mom, we're making headway," Ginger said one afternoon when I was in her bedroom fixing the hem of one of her skirts. "Listen to Mam-ma."

Mother was downstairs at the piano, playing her favorite classics and her earliest recital pieces. As we listened, she swung into the stirring chords of "Clayton's Grand March."

"Yes, it's a good sign, and she plays well," I agreed. Music had always been a part of Mother's life. She had taught it in the school at West Liberty for seventeen years until Dad's illness forced her to stop. As I listened, I remembered seeing her, a newspaper-boat-hat perched on her head, flourishing a make-believe baton, marching at the head of a group of youngsters. Each child made weird noises that no self-respecting musical instrument would have claimed. But she taught her pupils to appreciate music, and, regardless of talent, they learned rhythm and how to count time.

"It's the first time she's played like that since she's been here," Ginger said, "but, somehow, her playing sounds sad. It must be rugged to have to live in your child's home, sort of like riding in a car with someone you've taught to drive and having to keep your hands off the wheel." She giggled. "Dad would understand that. He still keeps his feet on an imaginary brake when I'm driving. One of these days he'll either break his toe or push through the floorboards."

In the months that followed, I redoubled my

efforts on Mother's behalf. Not only did I solicit her advice on practically everything I did, I really took it, telling myself this was only a temporary situation. I proceeded to lean over backward in this all-important game of compromise.

7

Queen Bee

I'm not sure just when our efforts became too much of a strain, but somewhere along the line we discovered that Mother was assuming the role of a queen with us as her faithful subjects. We had accomplished what we set out to do, but we hadn't anticipated the side effects. True, Mother seemed to feel more at home every day, but we were doing everything she wanted and doing it her way. It was no comfort to realize we'd brought this situation upon ourselves, and we didn't know what to do about it.

Since we treated Mother like royalty, she naturally responded in like manner. She would have been less than human if she hadn't, and when she reacted to anything, she never did it halfway. The role suited her perfectly, and she gloried in it; she was saving her beloved family from the consequences of their follies.

By current standards Mother was a prude, but it wasn't her fault: she was simply a product of her Victorian upbringing. I remembered that one of Grandma's favorite words was "don't." She told me so many things a proper young lady didn't do that I used to wonder if it were really worthwhile reaching such a lofty estate. According to Grandma, anything pleasant was sinful. Once, after I'd spent months learning to whistle, she told me, "A whistling girl and a crowing hen always come to some bad end."

A perennial do-gooder, Grandma spent the better part of her life going to church, sewing circles, quilting bees, prayer meetings and trying to keep Grandpa away from "The Bottle." Though I'm sure she loved him, Grandpa was the bane of her existence. Her older sister was another of her worries, for Great-Aunt Sally was vastly younger in thought and ways than Grandma. She even wore face powder, kept red peppermint drops to rub on her lips and used a burned match on her eyebrows.

I remember one time Mother brought Grandma and Aunt Sally to visit Dux and me in Kentucky. All the women in my family had small feet, and we were somewhat vain about them, but Aunt Sally especially was proud of hers and loved to buy fashionable shoes. One day when we were shopping, she noticed a sale at Bycks and went in.

"I'd like a pair of black patent leather pumps," she told the clerk, pulling up her skirt a bit for him to measure her foot.

"Sally, put your dress down!" Grandma hissed as the clerk left. "You ought to know better."

When he came back, Aunt Sally pulled her skirt higher and calmly ignored the remark.

Grandma squirmed.

"Ma, don't you want to try on a pair of shoes, too?" Mother asked. Grandma, acting very self-

conscious, looked uncomfortable, and when the salesman moved his stool in front of her and reached for her
foot, she jerked it away instantly.

"Get me a pair of black leather shoes with ties,
size 5B," she said. "I'll put them on myself."

Being a bit stout, she found it awkward unlacing
her old shoes without raising her dress. Finally,
realizing it was impossible, she stood up just as the
clerk returned with a pair of shoes for her.

"I've decided I don't need them," she announced
haughtily. "Let's go!"

Out on the street, Aunt Sally snapped at her.
"Whatever is the matter with you? That salesman is
probably laughing his head off. The idea! Why
wouldn't you let him put that shoe on your foot?"

"Because I believe in modesty. You ought to be
ashamed of yourself, showing your legs like you did."
Grandma retorted.

Aunt Sally tossed her head. "I'd rather show my
legs than to let him know I'm a backwoods hillbilly like
you just did."

A firm believer in hellfire and damnation,
Grandma brought up her seven children accordingly.
Mother must have been a satisfactory daughter, but
now she expected the same set of standards from us
and didn't hesitate to let us know it.

She was shocked that I served tall glasses of
Budweiser to Dux's friends when they were over for
poker. The very word "beer" offended her and card
playing was wicked. Finally Dux stopped inviting his
friends in for the evening, although I'm sure he hated
giving up those hours of fun and relaxation.

I, too, gave up cards to satisfy Mother because she
was horrified at my playing bridge for a quarter a
corner. That was gambling, and gambling was sin.

However, she didn't object to rook or flinch or checkers.

"But Mother," I pointed out, "you can gamble on any game."

"I suppose so," she conceded, "but those spot cards are bad, and I'm sure they've broken up many homes. Don't forget you have to set an example, not only for your daughter, but for your husband as well."

One night we gave a dinner party for an out-of-town visitor. Even though Dux and I didn't drink, we always served cocktails before dinner to our guests who did. Mother's disapproval of cards was mild compared to her feeling against hard liquor. Beer was bad enough, but whiskey was an abomination.

"It's the tool of the devil," she said and was so appalled that she actually took to her bed with a sick headache. Later, when I reluctantly assured her that it wouldn't happen again, she tried to console me by saying, "All they want is free liquor anyway. You're better off without those kind of people."

When my cigarette-smoking friends dropped in, I was on pins and needles, knowing Mother would show her disapproval. If she didn't say anything, she could be depended upon to go into fits of coughing, excuse herself and leave the room. Ashtrays began to disappear as if by magic, and matches, as well as lighters, were hidden away. Thanks to Mother, everything resembling temptation was put safely out of sight.

"Fire at one end and a fool at the other," she would quote after the smoker had gone. "It's bad enough for a man, but a smoking woman . . ." She'd shake her head as if the thought of it were too much for her.

It dawned on me that we were fast becoming an island unto ourselves with Mother waving the scepter as she'd waved the baton in earlier years. Just as she had instilled rhythm in her youngsters so she was trying to indoctrinate us in the twentieth century to live in a Victorian manner. Dux was trying his best to be a good sport through all of this, but I knew he wasn't happy.

"What about dancing, Chubby?" he asked one evening. "Any scruples against that?" I frowned at him, but Mother actually smiled.

"Ma wouldn't allow dancing, but I've always loved it." She giggled. "You know, that's the only thing I ever fooled her about. I'd tell her we played 'Happy is the Miller Boy' at parties, and she never did find out it was a dancing game."

"Well!" I shook my head at her. "I'm surprised, but it does show you're human after all."

"Of course, you can make harm out of anything," Mother qualified her remarks. "Dancing is all right in its place, but I don't believe in dancing on Sundays, and bodies shouldn't be too close together. I certainly don't like this modern jitterbugging, as Ginger calls it, and I don't approve of teen-age dances without chaperones."

She looked over at Ginger who was seated at a card table reading a book, but not missing a word of the conversation, I was sure. At this point, she snapped her book shut and stood up.

"I suppose I have to give up dancing now," she said with annoyance. "Old people just don't understand! I can't see what's wrong with it . . ." She broke off and left the room in disgust.

I think Mother's attitude toward Ginger irked me more that anything else. Ginger, christened Harriet Virginia, was Mother's namesake. Because Mother loved her dearly, she wanted her to be perfect, but nothing she did ever seemed to be right. Those embarrassing shorts, couldn't they be made longer? In her day, nice girls didn't cross their legs—they sat straight in a chair with their hands in their laps. That neckline, couldn't a pin close it up a bit? And surely, no nice girl would ever go alone with a boy in an automobile.

"Now, Mam-ma," Ginger had teased her, "don't tell me you had an automobile chaperone because they didn't have cars in your day."

"No, we didn't," Mother admitted, "but we had buggies, and we didn't ride alone with a young man until after the engagement was announced. We went in groups to picnics, candy-pulls, parties and hayrides, and we were always chaperoned."

"Yes," I put in, "I remember one time when I was a girl. My beau got up a hayride with two big wagons. He put all the chaperones in one wagon and the kids in the other, but no one realized it until afterward. We sang all of the old songs, and Bob kept his arm around me the whole time as we bumped over the dirt road. It was fun, and I don't think my reputation suffered. You don't want your granddaughter to be old-fashioned, do you?"

"I just want her to have ideals, to have a proper sense of values." She paused, then added, "What's the matter with being old-fashioned anyway? In my opinion, the world would be better off if we'd kept a few of the old ways."

She had something there, I thought. I smiled weakly and gave up.

8

Professional Jealousy

All his life Dux had loved boats; he'd even gotten his nickname from one. At sixteen, someone gave him an old wreck that he rebuilt and named "Dux" from the Latin word for "leader." His home was in New York, and he used to take kids sailing on the Hudson River for twenty-five cents an hour.

Because of his passion for boats, marine pictures always held a fascination for Dux. One Sunday afternoon, while wandering through an art museum, he was intrigued by a certain painting. It was simply a sailboat with a girl standing on the deck, and I couldn't see why it held his interest.

"See anything wrong with that?" he whispered to me.

"Certainly not! It was done by a well-known artist."

"I don't care who did it! He doesn't understand the principles of air movement. The wind is blowing the sail one way and the girl's skirt another. You know, Montague Dawson is the only marine artist whose pictures are truly authentic," he stated authoritatively. "Someday, when my ship comes in, I'm going to own a Dawson."

That's when I started my savings account, but after I learned the cost of Dawson's paintings, it almost seemed hopeless.

Later I met Dan Rees, an art dealer who could obtain a Dawson original. He would allow me to pay him in monthly installments, and I decided to get it for Dux's birthday.

The day Dan brought the painting to the house, I called Mother downstairs with a good deal of pride and satisfaction. The work was Dawson's interpretation of the race between the *Thermopylae* and the *Cutty Sark*, and the old china clippers looked as if they'd sail right into the living room.

"There, how's that?" Dan turned on the tiny electric light at the top of the frame and stepped back. "Like it?"

"Oh, it's beautiful!" I gasped, but I didn't tell him it was more than a picture to me; it was the fulfillment of a cherished dream.

Mother hadn't said a word, and I assumed she was as enthralled as I, but when the door closed behind Dan, she exclaimed, "So that's what you bought!" Her expression was a mixture of shock and reproach. "If you'd told me Dux wanted a picture of a ship, I could have painted him one and saved all that money."

Like many southern daughters, Mother had studied art as well as music in boarding school. She'd dabbled in oils, giving her pictures to various members of the family. Several of her drab efforts were in my attic.

"But, Mother, this is a Dawson!"

"I don't care what you call it, it's only a couple of ships on the ocean, and I could paint them as well as anybody." She looked at me accusingly, then added, "In fact, I've been meaning to ask you why you keep my paintings in the attic. The only ones you've hung are in the bedrooms."

My patience was fast giving out. "Mother, you don't understand. This is an original. This is art!"

"Fiddlesticks!" she snapped. "You think I don't know art? Why, I've painted for years."

"Then you ought to know this is professional," I burst out in exasperation. "You're good, Mother, but you're still an amateur."

"Well, I never!" She looked ready to cry. "So I'm just an amateur, I don't know art, and I'm too dumb to appreciate this old whoever-he-is." She sniffed and wiped her eyes. "I won't bother you with my work again. I'll get my pictures and give them to someone who won't hide them." She got up and left the room and I dropped into a chair.

All the joy in the picture was gone. A feeling of anger swept over me. I'm tired, I thought, bone tired—tired of having to weigh every word I speak to keep from hurting Mother's feelings, tired of not being myself, tired of being told what to do and how to do it. I sat staring at the painting, feeling sorry for myself. Now what, I wondered.

Suddenly I remembered what I'd always told my children to do when things looked black: "Count your blessings." How fortunate I was to have a mother at all! I thought of her courage in giving up her home, the wistful look on her face when she spoke of Dad. Her one thought now was to be helpful because she loved us.

I ran upstairs and into her room without knocking. Never as long as I live will I forget the sight of Mother sitting in the small rocker, her hands folded in her lap and her cheeks moist with tears.

"Oh, Mother, you've been crying." I threw my arms around her. "I'm so sorry."

She pulled me down on the footstool and touched my face. "I'm a silly old woman." She tried to smile, but her eyes were sad. "You and Dux are so good to me. I shouldn't have lost my temper."

"It was all my fault," I said apologetically. "I'll get your pictures from the attic right now. You come tell me where to hang them."

"No, dear, I'd like to take a nap," she said.

I looked at her quickly. It occurred to me that she hadn't seemed as chipper as usual today, but Mother never admitted to not feeling well.

"You're not ill, are you?" I put my hand on her forehead and it felt warm. She might have a fever. "Do you think you're coming down with something?"

"Of course not," she said with spirit. "I simply feel like taking a nap."

I tucked her into bed, kissed her and closed the door.

9

Dieting Dilemma

After weeks of pleasing Mother's palate, I was dismayed to see how many pounds she had gained since living with us. My concern was so great that I insisted on calling our family physician and friend, Dr. Lewis. Against her wishes, Mother finally submitted to an examination

"There's nothing seriously wrong, Mrs. Baldwin," he said at last, "but your blood pressure is high, and that's bad for your heart. You really should lose weight."

That night at dinner, Dux made a few kidding remarks as Martha served the corn pudding. "First thing you know, Chubby, we'll have to change your nickname to 'Humpty Dumpty.' Like Doc says, that excess fat is no good."

"It's glandular and it runs in the family," Mother

snapped back defensively. "Ma **was** always plump and Aunt Mary wore outsize stockings. Why, Pa said they had to make a special coffin for **Great**-Aunt Liza." She stopped a minute, then said reluctantly, "Well, I know I'm overweight. You get that way when you're alone and worried. What you eat goes to fat, and the more you eat, the more you want to eat. It's a vicious circle."

It was my conviction that many of Mother's excess pounds had been acquired during the past several weeks. The hot biscuits, gravies and luscious pies Martha had prepared in her all-out effort to please Mother and to show off her own culinary skill had a great deal to do with it. Almost every meal Mother would say, "I never eat more than three biscuits, but just this once . . ."

I kept my mouth shut. As Mother had often pointed out, there are times when silence is golden, but I decided to do something about her weight.

Saturday morning I helped Martha clear the refrigerator of all temptation, and that afternoon I tore around Jackson buying lavishly, if not always wisely, the low calorie foods. That evening I had to tackle the job of selling Mother on the necessity for reducing. It wasn't easy, but I assured her the whole family would help.

Monday morning we all started on the diet. Dux balked at first. He thought it was silly when the rest of us didn't need it, but I told him we should give Mother moral support and pointed out that the reducing books say it's hard to lose weight by yourself.

The diet list was tacked over the kitchen sink, and that night I heard Dux reading it with disgust in his voice. He then peered into the refrigerator which was practically bulging with health and vitality. Closing the door in disappointment, he asked, "What happened to the chocolate cake Martha made a couple of days ago?"

"There wasn't much left so I threw it away. You eat too much chocolate anyway."

"How about the peanut butter cookies?" he persisted. "Did you throw them away, too?"

"No, but I gave them to Martha for her church supper. She shouldn't have made cookies anyway because she knew about this diet business, but she felt sorry for Mother. Don't look so glum," I said trying to cheer him up. "You can still have cream in your coffee. The bottle's right there on the top shelf behind the skim milk and the unsweetened grapefruit juice."

"That's big of you, Shortie. Guess I haven't much choice." Without further comment, he helped himself to coffee, carried it into the den and drank it in silence.

At first, the demands of our diet didn't seem too

restrictive. Surely no one could go hungry with all that lean meat, fish, cottage cheese, fresh vegetables and pineapple, but after several days, everything began to taste pretty much the same.

By the early part of the second week, Dux took to eating his lunches downtown. Suddenly he had business deals to make over dinner, or so he said.

Russ, who had been coming home on weekends, also discovered other places to eat and I didn't blame him. He couldn't afford to lose weight while working so hard on the pipeline.

It also took the better part of valor to overlook Ginger's sudden interest in her friends around the dinner hour, although I did take her to task about the number of candy bar wrappers I found in her wastebasket. So much candy, I warned her, was not only bad for her complexion, it would ruin her teeth. Ginger, being a dutiful daughter, didn't argue the point, but the candy wrappers continued to appear occasionally, and once she confessed she'd eaten three desserts for lunch in the school cafeteria.

Meanwhile, Mother and I stuck to our guns. We sat together at breakfast, lunch and dinner, consuming low calorie health foods that included every vitamin known to man.

Martha wasn't much help to our worthy cause. She was afraid of diets and seemed to think they were a reflection on her cooking. Now and then she would say in a nearly apologetic tone, "Couldn't I just fix y'all a nice sweet potato pie—a little one with a mite of butter, brown sugar 'n stuff?"

"Certainly not," I'd say with all the firmness I could muster, "but thanks just the same."

"Certainly not, Martha," Mother would echo just as firmly, but I could tell she was fairly drooling.

At the end of seven days, I had lost 5 of my 115 pounds. My stomach was as flat as a pancake and I felt light as a feather, especially in my head. Mother, whose project this was supposed to be, hadn't lost an ounce!

"Well, I told you it wouldn't do any good," she said, stepping off the scales. "Like I said to the doctor, it runs in our family to be stout."

"Wait just a minute." I hurried into our bedroom for my reading glasses, unwilling to believe the awful truth. "Now get back on the scales," I told her and knelt down to squint at the figures—158 pounds—exactly her weight when we started the diet. I simply couldn't believe it!

"Ma was always plump," Mother was saying. "Aunt Mary wore . . ."

"Oh, yes," I interrupted, my impatience getting the better of me. "Aunt Mary wore outsize stockings, and they made a special coffin to hold Great-Aunt Liza. I heard that the first time you said it. It was their tough luck to be fat, but it doesn't have a thing to do with you."

"Well, I don't see why not," countered Mother, jerking the cord of her robe and tying it tight around her middle. "As I said before, you can't go against nature."

"Nature, my foot! I'm your kinfolk, too. Remember?"

"Reckon you take from your dad's side of the family," she said, falling back on an alibi familiar to parents. "Anyway, I was slim, too, at your age. Just wait until you get older and start thickening up."

My temper went. "That's nonsense. There's only one reason for being fat and that's not eating right. And don't talk about heredity and glands. You're exactly where you were when we started." I looked at her suspiciously. "You've been cheating!"

"How could I?" she demanded, looking hurt.

For the life of me, I couldn't see how or when.

We'd been together practically every waking hour, but why wouldn't we both lose weight when we'd eaten the same food?

"How could I cheat?" she repeated, indignantly now. "There isn't a piece of cake or a bit of candy in this whole house." She turned and started toward her room, indicating that the subject was closed as far as she was concerned.

At her door, she looked back at me. "Well, don't feel bad. You did the best you could." She closed her eyes and drew in her breath. "I'm going to tell Martha she can make that sweet potato pie with all the butter and brown sugar she wants."

"Oh, no, you won't!" I said firmly. "Tomorrow we start all over again—this time with smaller helpings."

The look of dismay on Mother's face would have been comical if the situation hadn't been so serious. As she went into her room, I heard her mutter to herself, "Why did the good Lord give us appetites if He didn't expect us to eat?"

When I told Dux about it, he said, "Can you blame her? No bread, no butter, no salt, and that fish tastes like sawdust. She's probably eating on the sly."

I shook my head. "I've been with her almost every moment. Besides, where would she get something fattening? There isn't anything but low calorie stuff in this house."

"Boy, don't I know that!" His words sounded grim even though he laughed.

"It's not funny. You know what the doctor said about her heart, but you don't help the situation one bit! You eat those gooey things downtown while I stay at home and eat sawdust with Mother." I was furious!

Dux put his arms around me, and I buried my face in his shoulder. "You shouldn't go overboard, Shortie. I do know Chubby has to lose weight, but can't she take it in smaller doses?" He kissed me sympathetically. "I want to help, but I don't know how. I'm really worried about you. You've been snappish all week."

What Dux said was true and I felt a stab of shame and guilt. I had been cross with him, and with Ginger, too. Chagrined, I resolved to turn over a new leaf.

That night I couldn't sleep. Remembering a book I'd been reading in the living room, I got up, found my robe and slippers in the dark and padded downstairs to find it.

As I reached the bottom step, I noticed a light in the kitchen. When I entered the room, I stopped abruptly and stared incredulously at the scene before me. There sat the object of my concern in her bathrobe and bedroom slippers, calmly pouring Dux's coffee cream over corn flakes.

"Mother!" I gasped. She jumped, spilling cream on the table and almost upsetting the bowl of cereal.

"You scared me, Winalee." She spoke accusingly even though she looked ashamed.

"You talk about nature and kinfolks and glands and how it's no use to diet, but look at you!" I scolded. "You said you didn't cheat. How long has this been going on?"

"Not long," she hedged. "I couldn't sleep so I thought maybe if I just had a bite of something . . ." She wouldn't look at me as she wiped the cream off the table with the torn half of a paper napkin. "Anyway, it's only a little cereal, and that's supposed to be good for you."

"How many nights have you been doing this, Mother?"

She stood up and faced me, a look of defiance in her eyes. "Now you listen to me, young lady! I'm sick and tired of that tasteless food."

"But Mother . . ."

"Don't you 'but' me, Winalee Gentry." She raised a

warning hand, and for an instant, I thought she meant to box my ears. "I'm hungry, so I'm going to eat, and I'm going to eat things I like."

I'd completely forgotten how Mother loved corn flakes and cream. Now I knew why Dux grumbled about the color of his morning coffee. Mother must have added skim milk to the bottle of shrinking cream.

"If I have to give up eating in order to live," she continued, "I'll just fold up right now and let Gabriel blow his horn. I know I haven't got much time left, but I'd give a year of it right now for a plate of hot biscuits and sorghum molasses and pecan pie! You wouldn't understand that. You're young, and you've got a home and a husband. Now just leave me alone."

With that, she sat down, pulled the bowl of forbidden cereal toward her, took a generous mouthful and gave me a look that dared me to take it away from her.

"Mother, please . . ." I began, but stopped. She had put her finger on one phase of her problem that I'd purposely ignored, feeling unable to cope with it. Somewhere I'd read that people overeat because they're lonely, unhappy or frustrated. It wasn't the food that was important, but the consolation that eating gave them. Mother never really complained, yet she must have spent many heartbreaking hours alone with memories of the happy life she'd lived with Dad in their own home.

Impulsively, I leaned over and kissed the top of her head. "All right. I'm sorry, but please go as easy as you can. You know what Dr. Lewis said about your heart. We'll try to find something interesting for you to do, something to take your mind off food and . . ."

"You don't have to find something interesting, as you call it. You haven't pulled the wool over my eyes one bit. I'm aware of how you've ganged up to let me run things, catering to me as if I were a spoiled child who had tantrums. From now on, you can run the house. I'm through."

71

When I started to protest, she held up her hand and stopped me. "Just leave me alone. I'll do the planning. I've always worked out my own problems—once I got mad enough!"

10

Harriet's Table Exercise

The next morning, much to my amazement, Mother resumed her diet, carefully avoiding any mention of the night before. We sat through breakfast in complete silence—not the silence of companionship and understanding, but a tense, uneasy silence.

Dux hid behind the front page of the newspaper as he had been doing so many mornings lately. Although he didn't say anything, I knew he was worried about the continued bombings of Britain. They had been going on since July and it was beginning to look like our boys would have to get involved.

Now and then I'd steal a glance at Mother as she munched away on dry whole wheat toast, acting like she really enjoyed it. Her expression reminded me of an overstuffed cat after a raid on a cream bottle, and with good reason, I thought crossly. Mother had not only lapped up the forbidden cream—she'd gotten away with it and somehow made me feel I was to blame.

Before breakfast was over, the doorbell rang. Ginger, still chewing on her coffee cake, ran to the door to meet her boy friend. This was the first day of her senior year in high school, and she could hardly wait to see all her friends.

Later Mother went up to her room, and the radio started blaring forth the strains of Don McNeil's Breakfast Club. Gratefully I turned to some papers Dux had left for my attention. In business affairs, at least, I was still regarded as a complete adult.

The morning hours flew. Suddenly I became aware of the ominously quiet house. I thought it was because I missed Ginger's lively presence, but then I realized that Mother's radio had stopped. A quick glance at the clock told me it was time for Ma Perkins, a program she couldn't bear to miss. Maybe she's ill, I thought. Maybe her gastronomic fling of the night before had caught up with her.

Frightened, I ran up to her room and put my ear to the door. There wasn't a sound. In sudden panic, I grabbed the knob. Just then the door jerked open from the inside, and Mother stood there calmly with a letter in her hand.

"Oh, Winalee! You startled me," she said. "I'm looking for Oswald." There was a smug expression on her face.

"Did you want Ozzie?" I asked lamely, still weak from fear and fright. "Can I do something for you?"

"No, reckon not. I have an important letter I want him to mail at the post office."

Holding out my hand, I said, "I can take it, Mother. I have to get the car out anyway to go for groceries right after lunch."

She shook her head and put the letter in her dress pocket before I could glimpse the address on the envelope. "No, thanks, dear. Martha said Oswald could go. And don't fix me anything to eat. I'm not hungry."

Without further ado, she went back into her room and closed the door. Clearly Mother was up to something, but I couldn't imagine what it was.

After Ozzie had taken the letter, Mother came downstairs and seemed so restless I thought perhaps hunger was bothering her. One minute she was reading a western; the next minute, crocheting. After a few rows, she abandoned that in favor of the piano and started running her hands fitfully over the keys.

"Mother, would you like a glass of skim milk? Or perhaps a few wheat crackers? Let's have a mid-afternoon snack."

"No, thanks. Reckon I'm unstrung—just can't seem to sit still."

I tried another tack. "Let me teach you how to play solitaire. It'll be good for you to rest your hands and take your mind off food."

As if I hadn't heard it all before, she started telling me what she thought of gambler's cards. "Anyway, I've heard that solitaire is called 'Idiot's Delight,' and I'm not ready for that, at least not yet." She took a handkerchief from her pocket and wiped her face. "A bit warm in here, isn't it?"

"What's wrong, Mother? I never saw you so jumpy." Then I thought of the letter. "Did you get bad news from Aunt Nancy or anyone back home?"

She shook her head, her fingers twisting the hand-kerchief in her lap. Her cheeks seemed unusually flushed, and I wondered what could be bothering her.

Then looking up quickly, she hesitated before saying, "Well . . . I might as well tell you." She giggled nervously, then added dramatically, "I've enrolled in a charm school."

"A charm school!" I repeated, aghast.

"That's what it's called. They've been advertising it on the radio. It's a course by mail, and they teach you how to diet, how to exercise, how to choose the right clothes, how to improve your personality and attract men."

"Attract men!" I laughed. "Tell me more. It sounds delightful!"

"Well, that isn't what I'm interested in. It's the reducing that appeals to me," she said demurely. "I've been thinking about it since last night because it seems like dropping a bucket into an empty well for me to keep on this diet. Most likely I need exercise, too. So I made up my mind I'd try this—but just for the physical culture, mind you."

"Oh, Mother, I'm so glad you did. I can hardly wait to see it."

"It'll give me something to do besides think about food and feel sorry for myself." Mother went on, a note of apology creeping into her voice. "You just can't break years of habit overnight. I've got a lot of energy for an old lady." She paused, then added cheerfully, "Honestly, I don't feel old at all."

"You're the youngest great-grandmother I know! You take this charm school course, learn how to exercise, how to choose the right clothes, but leave your personality alone. No one could improve on that."

We waited impatiently for the course to arrive. For Mother, the days passed as slowly as they had recently for Bud and Ruthmary before little "Hoddy" was born. Mother would bring her small radio and crocheting to the front hall where she'd sit hour after hour waiting for the postman. If she glimpsed him up the street, she'd hurry to the door. But the package didn't come. I was beginning to think Mother had been taken in by some New York "sharpie," but surely, I reasoned, Detroit's WJR would check their advertising.

Then one day when I was getting ready to go to the market, I heard Mother shout, "It's here, Winalee! It's here!"

I finished buttoning my dress, grabbed my purse and dashed downstairs. Mother, with shaking hands, was trying to open a package, mumbling something about tearing her fingernails to get charm. I ran to the kitchen to get a paring knife and slit the wrapper down the middle.

"Let's spread it out on the dining room table," I suggested. Mother pulled out the mimeographed pages of directions, illustrations of hair-dos, pictures of exercises for different parts of the body, and "before" and "after" photographs of women who had taken the course.

"*Features Particularly Adapted For Middle-Aged and Older,*" I read aloud. "Anyone can have a lovely figure, regardless of age." I tossed the pages on the table. "It sounds fascinating, Mother, but I've got to run to the store for a minute. Martha is in the middle of washing and just ran out of laundry soap."

She was so engrossed in the panorama before her, I doubted that she heard a single word I'd said.

All the way to the grocery store, I gloated. At last we've caught her interest, but not "we"—this was Mother's idea, her own decision. That would make the difference. Once she started a project, I was fairly certain she'd see it through.

I could remember her as she had been in my girlhood—slender, dressed in trim, swanky suits with perky hats to match. Drexel and I used to say we had the most stylish mother in the whole state of Kentucky. There was something so lively about her, the way she walked, the way her arms swung free, but mostly in the way she held her head up and her back straight.

Fifteen minutes later I returned with Martha's soap and hurried into the dining room. I stood spellbound for a few moments in the doorway, watching Mother seated at the table. Her eyes were closed, and her hands gripped the edge as she pushed back and forth from it, counting out loud.

"Mother! What on earth are you doing? Is this a part of your course?"

She stopped and looked at me in surprise. "I think so, although I don't understand it one bit! All the other exercises are so strenuous, but I could easily do this one in my room with my rocking chair and radio table," she ingeniously announced. "I've gone through the course and figured out how to do most of the exercises from the pictures, but this one doesn't have a picture." She picked up one of the pages and began to read out loud. "The very best reducing exercise of all is to push away from the table."

I flopped into the nearest chair and laughed until the tears rolled down my cheeks. "Oh, Mother, that's the funniest thing I've ever heard!"

"Well, I'm glad you think it's funny," she said huffily. "It just doesn't make any sense to me, and you don't either." She pulled her reading glasses down on her nose and frowned at me.

"I'm sorry," I said, trying to get myself under control. "I just can't help it! That's not an exercise, Mother, it's a play on words—you aren't supposed to take it literally. It means to push away from the table and stay there before you overeat."

Mother stared at me for a few seconds with a puzzled expression on her face. Then she threw up her hands and broke out laughing. "Land o' Mercy! Don't you dare tell this on me, Winalee. I wouldn't want anyone to know I was that dumb!"

11

The Sexy Blue Playsuit

Mother followed the diet and the exercises to the letter. As her weight went down, her spirits went up. So engrossed was she in her charm school course that she forgot to give us the benefit of constructive criticism, stopped telling us the correct time of day and hadn't mentioned the angel Gabriel in weeks.

Though reducing was no longer my project, I supported Mother until my clothes began to hang on me like gunny sacks. One night I slipped down to the kitchen when everyone else was asleep. Greedily I ate anything and everything I could find in the refrigerator, even filching a bit of Dux's coffee cream and then filling the small bottle with milk as Mother had done.

The days passed harmoniously. We exercised to music, sometimes with Ginger's record player. Mother followed each step with a determination that worried me, but when I timidly suggested that she take it a bit easier, she scoffed at the idea.

"I'm having a wonderful time!" she exclaimed. "You just haven't any idea what it means to lose those awful pounds."

Then she looked at me. "My goodness, Winalee, you're skinny! A stiff breeze would blow you away. Why in the world are you doing this?"

I looked at her in amazement. "Well, that's gratitude! Your course says it's easier to discipline yourself if you have company. Here I've been going through torment to help you—and you ask why!"

How the tables had turned, I thought. But with a happy sigh, I decided it wouldn't hurt to stop those tiring exercises and to eat what I liked. Both Ginger and Dux were pleased.

One morning after Dux had left for the office, Mother came downstairs carrying Ginger's portable phonograph and several records. Dressed in the blue playsuit I'd bought her, she looked like a plump little girl ready for a ballet lesson.

"I'm going to use the living room today," she announced. "My bedroom is too cramped for good leg exercises."

I helped her push the furniture out of the way and settled myself in a chair to watch. She got down on the floor—no easy task in itself—and lay flat on her back until she caught the beat of the music. Then, in complete rhythm, she started: left leg over—one, two, three, right leg over—one, two, three. Even though I'd been doing the same exercises, it was fascinating to watch her.

"I wish you'd let Dux see you go through these gymnastics," I said when she stopped.

She shook her head. "No man will ever see me in

my playsuit, let alone watch me work." The tone in her voice let me know there was no use in trying to persuade her otherwise.

Again outstretched on the floor, she turned, resting on her left side and elbow. Listening for the rhythm of the music, she raised her left thigh and began thumping it against the floor—thump, thump, thump—one, two, three. Then she turned on her right side: thump, thump, thump—one, two, three. She continued alternating sides until the music stopped.

Next she sat up with her legs straight out in front of her, and swinging her arms back and forth, she started to "walk" across the room on her fanny. I couldn't help laughing; she looked so comical in her efforts. After the panting stopped, she "walked" back, her rear rubbing along the carpet, her face flushed and her lips taut.

Suddenly there was a noise at the open window. It sounded suspiciously like a snort. Startled, I looked up in time to catch a glimpse of our handyman backing out of sight with his paint brush in mid-air.

"Ye gods and little fishes! It's Mr. Wickett!" I cried and ran to pull the draperies together. "I forgot that we asked him to paint the sills before winter set in."

Mother scrambled up with more speed than dignity and fled upstairs, leaving me to turn off the phonograph and push the chairs back into place.

A few minutes later, I was in the kitchen laughing and telling Martha about Mother's predicament when there was a light tap on the back door. It was Mr. Wickett.

"'Scuse me, Ma'am, but could I have a drink of water?" he asked in a shy, almost apologetic voice.

"Why, surely." I took a glass from the cupboard, put some ice in it and filled it with water. "Here you are," I said, trying to keep a straight face.

"Your ma's a right comely lookin' woman, Mrs. Gentry," he said looking down at the floor. "I been a widder nigh onto two years, and it's plum lonesome, 'tis." He set the glass down on the sink, then looked up at me. "I been lookin' fer a body to hook up with— 'tain't no fun goin' to a empty house." Turning quickly, he hurried out the back door, saying something about going back to work.

Laughing hysterically, I ran upstairs to tell Mother she had a suitor. "You should have heard him. You are comely and he is lonesome. Oh, never underestimate the power of a blue playsuit!"

"That's ridiculous!" she snapped. For once, Mother refused to see the humor of a situation.

During the following weeks, Mother exercised privately in her room. She had dropped twelve pounds of the forty that Dr. Lewis had said she should lose. For the first time in years she had the semblance of a waistline. Her clothes were beginning to look sloppy, and I suggested that we go shopping for a new dress.

"Not yet," she said. "When the spirit moves me, I'll splurge."

12

The "Spirit" Came In Pants

Mother had changed a lot in the last few weeks and we were grateful. If she still thought of Gabriel's impending horn, nothing was said. Not only did she look years younger, she acted years younger. Her renewed enjoyment of life delighted us.

Martha was on vacation, and I was in the kitchen one afternoon making a chef's salad when Mother came in.

"Did I hear you say someone is coming to dinner?" She broke off a piece of celery top and popped it into her mouth.

"Yes, Cecil Runyon from Port Huron. He's President of the Southeastern Michigan Gas Company, and Dux has built several pipelines for him. They've been friends for years."

Automatically I reached for the salt, then stopped.

Let them add it, I decided. Mother's charm course said that salt was one of the most fattening things of all. This sounded queer to me until I remembered that Grandpa always fed salt to his cattle before they were sent to market.

"We'd like you to meet Mr. Runyon, Mother. He's a charming man about your age." Noticing her expression, I hastily added, "He's married, of course."

The oven timer buzzed, and I opened the door, hoping the delicious smell of my chocolate cake wouldn't tease Mother's appetite.

"Well, I don't know," she said hesitantly as she closed her eyes and sniffed. "Maybe I'd better have a tray in my room."

"It's your decision," I told her. "We'd like to have you eat with us, and except for the cake, there isn't anything you can't have. Oh, yes, I forgot. I'm going to make hot biscuits for Dux."

"Well, I hope I'm boss of my own palate and can refuse to let it be tempted," she said firmly. "Reckon I'll join you."

"Remember, it's your choice."

"I know." Mother opened a drawer, took out a clean apron and tied it around her waist. "Now, what can I do to help?"

"You can set the table, if you'd like to. Get the lace cloth from the second drawer of the buffet." It had been a long time since we'd entertained, and because the dinner for Mr. Runyon was a special occasion, I wanted to use my best.

"Where did you get this thing?" Mother called from the dining room, and the disapproval in her voice was evident.

Puzzled, I walked to the door and saw her holding my lovely lace tablecloth in her arms, rubbing the corner between her thumb and forefinger. "Whatever you paid for this was too much," she scolded. "Didn't you know it wasn't handmade?"

"I don't care, Mother. That 'thing' happens to be my best tablecloth," I said crossly. I'd bought it from a peddler who told me it was his last one and that he'd sell it for half price. I liked it, even if I had been cheated, and it irked me to have my possessions belittled, but I kept my mouth shut.

"Just imagine, throwing out good money for a thing like this," Mother muttered as she threw the cloth over the mahogany table. Opening the top drawer of the buffet, she started taking out the silverware, still carrying on her running commentary.

Suddenly she pointed a fork at me. "Winalee, you buy me some number twenty crochet thread, and I'll make you a cloth you can really be proud of. I don't know why I didn't think of it before."

When the dinner hour arrived, Mother came downstairs wearing a black silk dress which was out of style and much too big. Her curly gray hair had been brushed up on top of her head, allowing her irridescent earrings to show. Right then I decided that she had to buy some new clothes and that they should be more colorful.

When I introduced Mother to Mr. Runyon, he gallantly remarked, "You must mean your sister, don't you?" Mother blushed like a schoolgirl, and I flashed our guest a smile of gratitude.

During dinner, Mother held her own in the conversation, and Mr. Runyon seemed responsive to her quick smile and friendly blue eyes. Every now and then she'd look at me, and I knew she was painfully conscious of the fact that she wasn't looking her best.

She ate the lean steak, broccoli without any hollandaise sauce and chef's salad with no dressing, but I noticed that she kept looking at Dux who was eating hot biscuits and gravy with obvious enjoyment.

The men were talking about football, discussing its

technicalities and wondering why Oklahoma lost to Texas.

"Winalee," Mother broke in, "how many calories would there be in just one little biscuit?" She had finished every scrap on her plate.

"Plenty. You said you wouldn't be tempted."

I turned toward Mr. Runyon and explained about Mother's reducing course.

He shook his head and smiled. "I know exactly what you're up against. My wife has been fighting a valiant, but losing battle with the scale for years. Sometimes I think it's a silly thing to worry about."

"Well, I've almost forgotten what Winalee's hot biscuits taste like," Mother said mournfully.

"Here, Mrs. Baldwin," Mr. Runyon said, passing her the plate of biscuits. "You deserve one and they really are delicious.

"The spirit is willing, but the flesh is weak," Mother quoted defensively as she helped herself to the largest one on the plate.

After we finished dinner, we set up the card table to play gin rummy. "Too bad Ginger had a date. We could have played bridge," I told Mr. Runyon.

He looked surprised. "You don't play bridge, Mrs. Baldwin?"

"Well . . . no," Mother said hesitantly.

Mr. Runyon smiled. "I didn't know there was a woman left in the world who didn't play bridge. My wife and her friends play all the time, even in tournaments."

Mother was obviously embarrassed. "You all go ahead with your cards. I'll just look on."

That's a switch, I thought. Never before had she been willing to watch a game played with wicked gambling cards, but now there was a look of interest on her face. As the evening progressed, she astonished me even more by asking a question now and then about the rules.

"I think you'd like gin rummy," Mr. Runyon told her. "It's easy to learn and fun to play. Besides, it's relaxing and a pleasant way to spend an evening."

Mother stayed downstairs with us longer than I'd expected, but somehow she seemed ill at ease and kept clearing her throat. Finally she excused herself, said good night and went up to her room.

The next morning I wasn't entirely surprised when she told me the game appeared harmless enough. "I reckon one could make evil out of almost anything, and it really doesn't seem fair to blame a deck of cards."

I grinned and hugged her. "You're getting smarter, Mother!"

There was a sparkle in her eyes as she went on, "You know, I've been thinking that I really do need some new clothes. It's been a mighty long time since I've had any pleasure in buying a new dress. What do you say we go shopping?"

I nodded and smiled at her. "We can go tomorrow." Inwardly I chuckled. Mr. Runyon had been the "spirit" that moved Mother.

13

Major Alterations

The day following Mr. Runyon's visit, Mother and I went shopping. After spending several hours choosing new fabrics and patterns, we looked at dresses in our best store. The salesclerk brought out a Persian blue silk with flared skirt.

"Oh, Mother, this is darling! Wouldn't you like to try it on?"

I turned to the clerk. "It looks just like her."

In the fitting room, Mother put on the dress and looked at herself in the long mirror.

"You'll have to shorten it, of course," I said, "but the style is very flattering. It's too bad the bust doesn't fit better."

"Well, that's one thing I can't help," Mother said, smoothing her hand down against her long, flat bosom. "I do like blue. This was the shade I was wearing when I met your dad," she said wistfully.

Suddenly an idea came to me.

"Mother, take off the dress and wait just a minute. I'll be right back." I hurried out of the fitting room and headed toward the lingerie department.

Upon my return, Mother was standing in her slip. Pulling her toward me, I pushed down the straps, took hold of her silk vest and jerked it over her head.

"What are you doing?" she gasped. "Is that curtain closed?"

"Yes, Mother, and I told the girl not to come in until we called her."

An expression of horror crossed Mother's face when she saw the brassiere. "I simply will not wear that thing. You were silly to buy it."

Ignoring her sputtering, I put her arms through the straps, then lifted her breasts one at a time, gently rolling each one up into the bra, and fastened the hooks in the back. "This will give you a much better figure," I said as I helped her put the dress back on. "There, don't you like that?"

"No, I don't! I look like a hussy, and I'm just not going to wear it." She was close to tears.

Somewhat discouraged, I shrugged and called the salesgirl.

"What an improvement!" she exclaimed. "The uplift makes you look years younger."

"I've never worn what you call an 'uplift' in my whole life, and I'm not going to start now." Mother said defiantly. "Look how it makes me stick out—it's not decent!"

I put my arm around her. "You look like a woman now, Mother. I'll bet it's been years since you've been aware of your breasts. They're flat because you've been pushing them down for so long, but they weren't like that when you were young."

Her lips quivered, but she didn't say anything.

91

"I don't know your real age, madam, but, honestly, you've got a better figure than half the women who shop here," the salesclerk volunteered, "and a good bustline is half the battle."

Mother was turning, first to one side and then to the other in front of the long mirror. Finally she stood still, and I wondered what her verdict on the new brassiere would be.

"What size is this dress?" she asked.

"Sixteen and a half," the girl told her.

She looked at me with a faint smile. "Well, I never thought I could look like this at my age. I reckon you're both right, but it's going to take a long time for me to get used to sticking out."

When we got home, Mother took the dress from the box and held it up in front of her, caressing the soft folds. "I'll go upstairs and fix the hem, but the neck seems too low, especially with that new thing."

That night she wore the dress down to dinner, but, as I'd expected, there was a white lace handkerchief across the neckline. It would take a long time for her to forget her early training, and maybe the alluring new cleavage would never be seen.

"Wow!" Ginger said. "Mam-ma, you look terrific!"

Dux gave a wolf whistle and pulled her chair out. "Chubby, where have you been hiding those boobs? Boy! Now you've really got a figure!"

Mother blushed. "You're both ladling out applesauce, but I love it."

The next morning I was measuring coffee for breakfast when Ginger came into the kitchen.

"Hi!" she greeted me. "What's happened to Mam-ma? How come she changed her mind all of a sudden?"

"You mean her new bust?" Absently, I plugged in

the percolator. "It'll take awhile for her to get used to the change."

"No, not that. When I came out of the bathroom this morning, she grabbed me, pulled me through her door and shut it. Then she whispered that she wanted me to teach her to play gin, but she called it 'rummy.'"

"Of all things!" I gasped. "And after everything she has said about those sinful face cards!"

"Don't let her know I told you," Ginger warned. "Although she didn't say not to, I wouldn't have mentioned it except I was afraid you'd wonder, because we'll probably lock the door for two or three hours in the afternoon."

I laughed to myself. Mother's education had started, and it ruined one of her favorite sayings, "You can't teach an old dog new tricks."

One morning at breakfast, a couple of weeks later, I asked Mother how she was coming with my tablecloth. I'd bought the number twenty thread, and she'd started it soon after Mr. Runyon was here.

"Oh, so-so," she answered evasively. "With all these exercises, I don't have much time to crochet. Anyway, my fingers get a little numb sometimes."

Probably from shuffling those sinful gambling cards, I thought gleefully. I began to count the women around Mother's age whom I knew; practically every one of them played cards. It would be such fun to give a party for her. Knowing her quick learning capacity, I didn't have a doubt that she'd be able to hold her own with the best of them.

"How's she doing?" I asked Ginger that evening after she'd had an unusually long session with Mother.

"Slow, but sure, as Mam-ma would say. She keeps telling me that 'Practice makes perfect' and that she'll get it eventually, but the trouble is that she wants to learn all the card games at once—not only gin, but bridge and canasta, too."

"That's a good sign, but she'll have to take them one at a time. Oh, she'll have so much fun once she gets started."

"I don't know, Mom. She doesn't seem to be having much fun now because she's trying too hard. She's so eager to learn, but she's fighting her conscience. I notice that when we're through, she always picks up her Bible."

I had suspected for some time that Mother had been struggling with a guilt complex, even though there was a look of defiance in her eyes. It was bound to be difficult, I thought, trying to change one's whole concept of life after years of adherence to a strict set of morals.

That night after we'd gone to bed, I talked to Dux about Mother. "Maybe we're wrong in trying to influence her. The conflict in her mind might even make her sick."

"Look, honey, you stop worrying. Chubby will work out her own problems. She always has. No one can make her do anything she doesn't really want to do."

At breakfast the next day, Mother seemed preoccupied. Usually she was talkative in the morning, wide awake the moment she opened her eyes, but today she hardly said a word, and, without waiting for her second cup of coffee, went right back to her room.

All morning I kept thinking about Mother. Trying to take my mind off of her, I got out the vacuum cleaner and started on the living room rug, but the gnawing anxiety wouldn't go away. I felt so helpless! It would be such a comfort to talk things over, I thought, but I couldn't betray Ginger. If only Mother would confide in me! Maybe she would, if I gave her the chance. I shut off the vacuum and ran upstairs.

"Listen tomorrow to Helen Trent," the radio announcer said, and I smiled indulgently.

"Mother," I called in a cheerful voice as I tapped on the door. The radio clicked off, and I heard the swish of movement, but it seemed a full minute before the door opened.

"Come in, dear." Her voice sounded shaky, and she cleared her throat. Although I saw her crocheting on the card table, I felt quite sure she hadn't been working on my tablecloth. Smoothing back her hair with an embarrassed gesture, she said, "Want something?"

"No, not a thing. I thought maybe you were lonesome up here by yourself and might like to visit."

I sat down on the bed. Mother didn't look like a woman wrestling with her conscience; she looked like a woman who'd been playing solitaire and almost got caught in the act!

"Honey, I'm never lonesome when there's something to do." She cleared her throat again. Casually she took off her glasses, polished each lens, and held them up to the light. Then, picking up the neglected crocheting, she began to work. "I'll be down in time to help with lunch." She smiled innocently, but I detected an air of victory in her look.

Nodding wordlessly, I gave up and left the room.

Dux was right again. Mother was doing what she wanted to do. Although struggling with her Victorian morals, she was determined to change her life, and I knew she would succeed in her own time without any help or sympathy from us.

14

The Holy Competitor

In the excitement of Roosevelt's election for an unprecedented third term in office, everything else was temporarily forgotten. Dux and I had hoped Wilkie would win, but because of the war, maybe it was better we didn't have a change.

A few evenings after the election, the Bushes came to dinner. Nellie May and Emerson had been our closest friends for years, probably because they'd lived in Kentucky, and Mother seemed more at ease with them than anyone else we knew.

After dinner, the two men went into Dux's den to talk about politics and the election. Contrary to her usual habit of leaving us alone with our friends in the evening, Mother joined us in the living room.

"Nellie May," she said unexpectedly, "do you play Canfield? It's a good game and a wonderful way to pass the time."

"Mother!" I gasped before Nellie May could answer. I was so astonished at her words that I didn't have to pretend surprise. "You mean you've learned to play solitaire?"

She grinned at me. "You think I'm not smart enough? It's fuel for the mind, it makes you think, and besides, it's a good way to spend a dull evening."

Nellie May laughed. "With a husband and three active boys, my evenings are anything but dull. It's all I can do to get in a bridge game now and then."

"Of course, you young people are busy. You wouldn't know about having time on your hands," Mother said woefully.

"We can teach her to play bridge," Nellie May put in quickly, looking at me. She turned to Mother and gave her knee an encouraging pat. "Mrs. Baldwin, you'd love bridge and you could belong to a club. There's a group of women around your age that meets twice a week."

Mother shook her head. "No, I reckon not. I'm too old, and I've been told it takes years of practice." Then her face brightened, and she said, "But I can play rummy—gin rummy, I mean. Why can't we have a game right now?" She looked at me as if she thought she'd exploded a bombshell, and indeed she had.

"You absolutely amaze me!" I jumped up and threw my arms around her. "I think you're wonderful!"

She laughed. "I knew you'd be pleased. Come on, girls, let's have a three-handed game."

"Mrs. Baldwin, I don't really know any card games except bridge," Nellie May confessed. "The only other game I've ever played was checkers."

Mother pounced on that. "Oh, good! I've always loved checkers. Dad and I used to play almost every evening." She got up and went to the card table in the corner of the room. "Get out the checkerboard, Winalee."

"I'm afraid you're in for a disappointment," Nellie May said apologetically. "I haven't played in years."

Mother was not to be dissuaded. "I haven't played in a coon's age myself."

I racked my brain trying to remember where we'd put the checkerboard. The kids used to play, but I couldn't think where or when I'd last seen it. Running up to the attic, I searched through Monopoly, Crokinole, Parcheesi and other games they had outgrown, but there was no checkerboard.

Reluctantly I returned to the living room. "I can't find it, Mother. I'm so sorry."

"Never mind. We're wasting time. I'll make one myself," she said briskly and hurried from the room. Back she came with a ruler and pencil in one hand and a large piece of cardboard in the other. "I remembered seeing this cardboard in the basement when you unpacked your new dishes," she told me with a satisfied smile. "Now you girls visit while I work."

We watched her rule off the squares, going over the lines again and again until they were dark enough to be clearly seen.

"Such ingenuity!" Nellie May laughed.

"Necessity is the mother of invention," Mother said, sounding as if she had coined the phrase.

"Could it be the other way around?" I joked. "Mother is the necessity for invention?"

"There!" Mother held up the board. "Now, we're ready."

"But what will you use for checkers? Nickels? Quarters? I don't think we'll have enough between all of us," I told her.

She smiled knowingly. "Go get your button box."

Even though I doubted that there would be many big buttons in it, I brought the box and dumped the contents on the evening newspaper. After sorting through all of them, I said, "There aren't enough. I can only find seven large ones."

"What's going on here?" Dux called from the doorway. He and Emerson walked over to see Mother's handiwork. "Not bad, Chubby," he said.

"No checkers, though," I told him, sliding the buttons from the paper back into the box.

"Why don't you get the poker chips?" he said casually.

"Why, of course!" I exclaimed. "Why didn't I think of that?" I started toward the closet where the chips were kept, but Mother stopped me.

"No, Winalee," she said and started to get up from the card table. "You folks go ahead and play bridge."

"Oh, no, you don't," Dux teased, pushing her back into the chair. "You don't get away that easy. I remember Dad telling us what a mean game of checkers you play."

"Oh, Dux," Mother said, "I don't mind playing. It's just those . . . those gambling things . . ."

"Mother," I broke in, "as long as you're not using them to gamble, what harm is there?" I began placing the blue poker chips on her board.

"All right," she conceded, sounding relieved. "I guess one game won't hurt."

Emerson helped me finish putting the chips on the board while Dux sat down across from Mother and jokingly rubbed his palms together.

The next ten minutes passed in silence except for the peculiar grunts Dux made each time Mother jumped his poker chip men. After taking his last two chips in one final triumphant jump, Mother let out a giggle.

"That'll fix you, Dux Gentry," she said, starting to put the chips back into the box.

"Maybe for now," he grinned, "but just you

wait . . ."

"That was good playing, Mrs. Baldwin," Emerson said, patting Mother on the shoulder.

"Well, I've had lots of practice." She got up to leave. "Now you all have your bridge game. I'll go up and get my crocheting."

"Don't go yet, Mrs. Baldwin. Play something for us on the piano first," Nellie May begged.

Surprisingly enough, Mother agreed. "I'd love to. What would you like to hear?"

"Play anything you want," she said, "and I'm sure we'll love it."

Mother sat down at the piano and began running through arpeggios, her fingers confidently touching the keys. Then the sparkling lilt of "Rustle of Spring" filled the room. It was the first time she'd played for guests since she came to live with us. Completely absorbed in the music, she continued on, oblivious to her audience until the dramatic finale when Ginger entered the room.

As Mother turned to get up, there was a chorus of protests. Ginger hugged her and said, "Oh, please, Mam-ma, play the one I liked so much the other night."

She smiled and began playing "Clair de Lune" with great sensitivity and warmth. As I listened to her, my mind went back to the night of her recital at the Louisville Conservatory of Music and the events leading up to it.

When Mother was paralyzed after Russell's birth and the doctors urged her to keep busy, she returned to the music she'd studied as a girl. Throwing herself wholeheartedly into her work, she sometimes would practice five hours a day.

At first, she didn't seem to mind walking with a

brace, but the thought of her upcoming recital made her worry about the looks of that heavy black brace on the new shoes she had bought. It was then that she learned to walk without it. Day after day, in the privacy of her bedroom, she practiced. In the beginning, she could only take a step at a time, but as she gained more confidence, she was able to make it across the room.

On the night of her recital, Dad, Drexel, Dux and I sat in the front row of the auditorium. We were astonished to see her tiny figure, dressed in light blue with matching slippers, walk slowly out on stage. She was a bit wobbly, with one foot dragging somewhat, but she held her head high and had a smile on her face.

When the familiar tones of her piece died away, there was a burst of applause. Mother must have been so engrossed in her music that she'd forgotten the absence of the brace. Springing to her feet, she bowed and started off the stage. One of the men in the wings caught her as she began to fall.

We hurried backstage, and Dad was the first to reach her. "Oh, my darling! You can walk!" he exclaimed, cradling Mother in his arms. "My precious 'Kewpie doll'!"

"I didn't tell you because I wanted it to be a surprise," she said happily. "At first, I was so scared, but now . . . oh, you can't possibly imagine how wonderful it is!"

"It's a miracle!" I said, daring to breathe again. "An answer to prayer!"

"You're absolutely right, Winalee. More things are wrought by prayer than this world ever dreams of," she said with conviction.

Later Dux confided to me, "I don't doubt for a minute that it was an answer to prayer, but I'll bet her vanity and those small feet had a lot to do with it."

The strains of "Let Me Call You Sweetheart" brought me abruptly back to the present. We all gathered around the piano and sang as Mother played ballads, popular songs and old familiar hymns. Whenever she could, Ginger joined in, but many of them were written long before her day—or even mine.

When Mother swung into "My Old Kentucky Home," we smiled as we knew it to be her favorite. These old tunes brought back memories of long ago when Dad, Drexel and I used to gather at Mother's upright piano while she played every song she knew. Both Dad and Drexel had fairly good voices, and often our neighbors would come up on the front porch to listen. This was the kind of evening Mother loved best. Why hadn't I remembered?

Suddenly, with characteristic time consciousness, she broke into "Good Night, Ladies," and that ended the evening.

The following night, Dux came home early with a smartly wrapped package under his arm. Winking at me, he turned toward Mother.

"This is for you, Chubby."

"For me? Oh, for goodness sake!" Excitedly she tore off the wrapping and held up a checker game. "Oh, Dux! You're wonderful!" She reached up and kissed him. "Let's have a game right now."

"Not so fast, Chubby," he grinned. "I'll play on one condition, and that's ten cents a game."

Mother winced. Then, reluctantly she said, "You drive a hard bargain, Dux. You know how I feel about gambling, but you never give up, do you? You'll make a sinner out of me yet," she added, with a twinkle in her eye. "Oh, well, since you were good enough to get it for me, I guess a little sin once in a while won't hurt me."

Eagerly, Ginger and I hovered over the card table, watching their contest without saying a word. Mother won game after game and the dimes piled up. But, gambler that he was, Dux kept trying to regain his losses until Martha called us to dinner.

After we finished eating, Mother excused herself and left the room before we did. When we came into the living room a little later, she was sitting at the card table, reading her Bible.

"Holy smokes, Chubby!" Dux yelled. "Put that Bible down. I can't beat you and God, too!"

With that, Ginger and I broke out laughing, but Mother and Dux seriously resumed their game, playing until bedtime. Dux won a few of their matches, but I noticed that Mother left all her earnings on the table.

15

An Influencing Figure

"Nancy wants me to come back to West Liberty for Christmas," Mother told me one day soon after Thanksgiving. "Said they all miss me and hope I can spend the holidays there. Nancy wants me to see her chicken farm, too. Every one of her letters is full of chickens, and last year she made enough on her fryers to buy that highboy she'd been eyeing for months."

"Why don't you go, Mother? Think of the fun you'll have showing off your new figure!"

"Well, reckon I would like to see everyone." She chuckled and pulled her belt a full inch tighter. "Won't they be surprised to see this?" she bragged. "But, Winalee, I only have one dress that fits me."

"Don't worry about that, Mother. If you want to go, we can have you ready in less than a week."

The next day we set up the sewing machine and

went to work, altering three of her old dresses and starting on two new ones. Then one afternoon we went downtown shopping, and Mother came home with a smart navy wool suit and matching accessories.

When she was finally ready to leave for Kentucky, Mother was as eager and excited as a young girl going on her first trip. We had suggested that she take a plane, but she wouldn't hear of it.

"Oh, no," she said emphatically. "I always love a bus. We all get acquainted and have lots of fun. Besides, it's cheaper."

A few minutes before we left for the station, Ginger handed Mother a small box with a necklace and matching earrings, a "going away" present from the three of us.

"Oh, you're all just wonderful to me!" she told us appreciatively. "I'm so thrilled to be going back to Kentucky, I hope I haven't forgotten anything." She ticked off items on her fingers, ending with, "Lee gave me little Jimmy's picture to show everyone." Starting to pull on her gloves, she said, "Well, reckon I'm all set."

"I'll bet a nickel you forgot your cards," Dux teased her. "You never can tell when you'll get the itch to gamble."

"That's a nickel I'd get!" Mother said as she took a playful swipe at him with her handbag. "As a matter of fact, Dux Gentry, I did slip some cards into my suitcase, along with my Bible."

Our house was strangely quiet, even lonely, after Mother left. Since she had been with us, our lives had been anything but dull, for she could always be counted upon to create a diversion. She could be sweet enough to melt the heart of a tax collector or as irritable as a saint's hairshirt!

We waited impatiently for her first letter. When it arrived, it was full of the excitement of being back in West Liberty, the parties given for her and the remodeling of the old Christian Church. Grandma had been an important figure in all the projects of that edifice, so naturally Mother was interested in it also.

During Grandma's lifetime, converts were baptized in the river during the summer, and these special events, which were followed by picnics and games, always drew crowds from quite a distance. Now, according to Mother's letter, they had started to build a baptistery inside the church.

"It will be the first one in town," she'd written, "and it will most likely be the nicest in the whole state."

Nowhere in this letter had she mentioned her weight, nor did she in any of the following letters that gave such glowing accounts of the local festivities.

"Those parties will ruin her figure," I lamented to Dux. "Mother's too polite to refuse anything her friends cook for her. I just hope she won't regain all those pounds she worked so hard to lose."

Dux laughed. "Don't worry, honey. Chubby's got too much pride to allow herself to outgrow her new clothes."

The only reference to diet in her letters involved Aunt Nancy's chickens.

> "I'm beginning to get tired of them.
> We eat them baked, boiled, fried
> and stewed, but mostly stewed
> because Nancy doesn't like to kill
> them until they're too old to lay."

It wasn't until the last of February that she wrote about her weight.

> "At first, I did gain a bit with all
> those wonderful parties, but I'm all
> right now. Almost every woman

around my age was too heavy, and I
knew something had to be done. I'll
tell you about it when I get home."

That word "home" brought tears to my eyes and
gave me such a sense of satisfaction. Gratefully I
realized the progress we'd made, and I knew our
meeting at the bus station this time would be a joyful
one, a complete contrast to the traumatic experience of
a year ago.

Mother came home on a cold and windy March
day. She had stayed in West Liberty longer than any
of us had expected, and we were glad to see her again.

"It's good to have you back!" I hugged her. "You
look wonderful, and I don't think you've gained a
pound."

Mother laughed. "Well, I can see why most of my
friends in West Liberty are fat. They love parties, and
each one was trying to outdo the other on the food.
After a couple of weeks, I decided to show them my
course and was able to get fifteen of them interested.
I said it wasn't their clothes that needed alteration—it
was their figures. When Christmas was over, they
asked me to write New York and order charm courses
for all of them. I was planning to come home in
January, but they begged me to stay and help with the
exercises."

"Imagine that!" It was hard for me to believe.
"You got all those women to start reducing?"

"None of them had worked that hard in years, but
I'll have to give them credit. They stuck it out. Now
everybody in West Liberty is talking about it."

Dux said he thought the charm school should give
Mother a commission and I agreed with him.

That weekend all the children came home to
welcome the returned traveler. Our house bulged with
people, and we stepped over blocks and a wooden

train, but we didn't mind the clutter—not even when neighbors dropped in to say hello.

After dinner Saturday evening, when the two babies had been tucked into bed, Mother told the children about her Kentucky visit and the fifteen women she had influenced to take the New York course. She talked about the new baptistery, and then started in on Aunt Nancy's chickens until we were completely bored.

The conversation finally returned to other channels, but Mother more than dominated the gathering that night. What a joy it was to have her home! Until now, we hadn't realized how much we'd missed her.

16

A Slick Chick

On a thawing, spring-like Monday in early April, Mother and I drove to "Sandy Cove," our new lake cottage in northern Michigan.

When Dux had first suggested the idea of buying this place, I questioned the wisdom of owning two homes.

"This summer I will be spending most of my time on the pipelines we have under contract in that area," he said. "I could fly to the cottage almost every night, but I could only get to Jackson on weekends. Besides," he went on, "this will be a good investment. Sage Lake is hardly built up at all and waterfront lots are increasing in value." Then his face lit up as he added, "And there's even a tool shed on the property."

That cinched it for me. Being able to work with his hands had always meant relaxation for Dux and had often been the means for getting rid of petty grievances. With such a busy summer in store for him, a workshop would be a welcome haven.

So now we were on our way to clean the cottage and fix up the old furniture we'd bought with it. Mother can use her painting talent on wood instead of canvas, I thought. I'd purchased fabric for slipcovers, and she'd promised to show me how to give them a professional touch.

Just as we were pulling into the little town of Sterling, Mother cried out, "Stop, Winalee! Stop!"

I jammed my foot on the brake pedal. "What is it? What's wrong?" I shouted, my heart in my mouth.

"A sign back there said, 'Fresh Eggs'," Mother told me calmly. "Back up! I want to get some."

Completely exasperated, I did as I was told. Mother went in, and I waited impatiently in front of the hatchery, anxious to get to the lake after such a long drive. I couldn't figure out why on earth she wanted to buy eggs when she hardly ever ate them. Finally she came out with an egg carton in one hand and a bunch of pamphlets in the other. There was an expression on her face that reminded me of the "cat that swallowed the canary."

"I got these pamphlets about raising chickens. You know, Nancy is doing such a good job, and she said it's because she reads all the scientific facts about diseases and other things."

For the next half hour we rode in silence while Mother read the leaflets. I was still a little annoyed over the delay and could care less about chickens.

Driving over the winding dirt road to the cottage, we could see the lake through the birch trees. I smiled to myself, remembering the first time I ever saw a grove of white birch. "Who whitewashed all those trees?" I said in my ignorance.

A doe and fawn crossed in front of the car,

stopping to stare at us curiously. Mother started to open her window, but at the first sound, they leaped out of sight. Continuing slowly on the narrow road, we rounded the bend and drove up to the door of our new home.

"It's hard to realize this belongs to us."

"Yes, and that tool house is even bigger that I imagined," Mother said, nodding her head with satisfaction.

I looked at her quizzically. Why would she be so interested in Dux's tool shed?

I built a fire in the old-fashioned wood stove and then started emptying the car while Mother unpacked the boxes of food, put on the coffeepot and made sandwiches.

We ate lunch in front of the living room window so we could look out over the water. Although it was too early for most cottagers, occasionally we could hear the hum of a motor and see a boat cut across the lake, leaving a wake of foam and bubbling white waves.

Full of energy and ambition after lunch, both of us went to work. Mother's singing, peculiarly her own, filled the room as we painted. I had always been able to gauge her mood by her songs, the gayer she felt, the sadder her lyrics. The "Letter Edged in Black" and "Highland Laddie" were two of her old favorites that I remembered from childhood. Even though I knew they indicated Mother was happy, they still had the power to bring tears to my eyes.

By the end of the week, we had things pretty well in hand. My slipcovers looked better than I'd imagined they would, and all the second-hand pieces of furniture, freshened with paint, appeared as if they'd just been delivered from the store. Mother was finishing the last chest of drawers late Friday afternoon.

"Ready to sit down with a cup of hot coffee?" I asked as she put the lid on the paint can.

Shaking her head, she gathered up the brushes, paint and rags and lifted the key ring off the rack. "Wait until I clean these paint brushes," she said hurriedly. "There's turpentine in the tool house."

All of a sudden it dawned on me that she was finding every imaginable excuse to visit Dux's workshop. Why couldn't she use the bottle of turpentine in the kitchen? What could she be up to? That place belonged to Dux, and he wouldn't like having his domain invaded. After a few moments, I followed discreetly and waited outside, but could hear nothing. Impatiently, I shoved back the door and went in. There stood Mother, tying a cloth over her hair, a broom resting against her body.

"What in the world are you doing?" I demanded.

Mother looked startled, but quickly recovered and said casually, "Oh, I just thought I'd clean this shed up a bit. It's high time somebody did. I never saw such a mess!"

"I don't think Dux would want it cleaned," I told her. But it didn't look very inviting, I had to admit. Old, dusty tools were scattered over the work table; a dirty barrel stood in the center of the room with a plastic-covered jigsaw next to it; cobwebs were everywhere, but why would Mother want to bother? I looked at her suspiciously. Then I smiled—it really was sweet of her to want to help Dux, and surely it wouldn't hurt to sweep out the dirt.

"All right, Mother, but remember you're treading on sacred ground, and be sure to put everything back the way it was."

Dux and Ginger were planning to arrive sometime that evening. It was Ginger's spring vacation, and we were looking forward to ten carefree days together. Because she would graduate in June and be away at college next year, we wanted to make the most of having her with us.

It was close to nine o'clock when we heard the car. Mother beat me to the door.

"Hi, you two! We thought you'd never get here," she cried excitedly. She kissed Ginger, grabbed Dux's hat, took the newspaper and magazines he'd brought and squeezed his arm. "Oh, my, I'm happy to see you."

"What a welcome, Chubby!" Dux laughed and hugged her. "You'll have me believing you really missed me." Glancing around the room, he added, "Boy, have you girls worked!"

"I'll say!" Ginger's eyes quickly took in everything. "This place looks terrific."

Well, we've spent a lot of time on it," Mother said, pushing the most comfortable chair closer to the crackling fire. She shoved a footstool in front of it and motioned for Dux to sit down. Then hurrying from the room, she called over her shoulder, "Don't go away, Dux, dear, I'll be right back."

"How come Mam-ma's making such a big deal over Dad?" Ginger asked perceptively as she flopped down on the rug in front of the fireplace.

"I was wondering the same thing myself, but I guess we'll know pretty soon." I turned to Dux. "Could I fix you anything to eat, honey?"

"No, thanks, Shortie. We ate in Standish." He flung a birch log on the fire and stood watching it until it burst into flames. "What'll you bet that Chubby has something up her sleeve—I seem to recognize the signs of 'molasses.'" He looked at me and winked.

In a few moments, Mother came back and handed Dux two pipes. "I found these in . . . er . . . they were dirty and smelly, so I scraped and scrubbed them for you. Now, they're like new."

An expression of horror crossed Dux's face. "Thanks, Chubby." He laid the pipes on the table and took an old one from his pocket. "I'll save the clean ones for later," he hedged.

Mother hovered over him like a brood hen all evening, looking as if she wanted to say something, but didn't quite know how to begin. When the fire died down, I suggested we all go to bed, and reluctantly, she said good night and went to her room.

The next morning, Dux and I awoke to a tantalizing aroma of coffee and bacon drifting in from the kitchen. He sniffed, grabbed his robe and pulled the covers off me.

"Come on, Shortie. Oh, boy! That smells delicious!"

Mother was pouring coffee when we came into the kitchen. As usual, she looked crisp and neat with a frilly apron tied around her waist. Caring how you look is no small part of growing old gracefully, I thought. Many times I'd come to breakfast looking like an unmade bed, but not Mother! She came downstairs in the morning, completely dressed for the day, even with a necklace and earrings.

"You amaze me," I told her one day. "If the doorbell rings, I scram out of sight, but if someone asked you to go to Timbuktu, you'd only have to grab your hat."

Mother laughed. "Ma wouldn't allow us to wear even a kimono outside our bedrooms, and we had to be fully dressed for the day when we came to breakfast. It's just habit, I reckon. 'Train up a child . . .' You know what the Bible says."

Too bad that training hadn't worked for me, I thought, but then, Mother was never as strict as Grandma, and I'd been even more lenient with my girls. As Mother often said, "The world would be better off if we'd kept a few of the the old-fashioned ways."

Mother handed Dux a cup of coffee, fawning over him. "Plenty of cream and two lumps of sugar—just the way you like it," she said sweetly. "I thought you'd never get up. I've been awake for hours. Everything's ready whenever you want it."

She had fixed a hearty breakfast of oatmeal, broiled bacon and scrambled eggs. For a woman who didn't like to cook, she could toss up a pretty good meal.

I knew Mother was up to something, but after we'd finished eating and started the dishes, she seemed completely unnerved. Finally she dropped a platter.

"What's the matter, Mother? What's bothering you?" I asked her as I swept the broken pieces into the dust pan. "You'd better tell me—I know something's wrong."

"No, there's nothing wrong." She paused and looked down at the floor. "It's just that . . . well . . . I've got a wonderful idea, but I need Dux's tool shed, and . . ."

"Oh, for heaven's sake!" I said. "You can stop right there. That's private property and strictly belongs to Dux."

"But he won't be able to use it this summer with all those pipelines, and what if he gets that job in Canada he was talking about? Anyway, I'm going to ask him, but I just want to make sure it's the right time when I do."

"You might as well save your breath," I told her flatly. "Dux isn't going to give up his workshop for anybody—not even you."

"Well, I can try." She smoothed back her hair and straightened her shoulders.

Just then, Dux came into the kitchen and stopped at the sink for a drink of water.

"See you later, gals," he said and started for the door.

"Wait a minute, Dux. I want to ask you something." Mother bravely walked up to him and put her hand tenderly on his arm. "I cleaned your tool shed and . . ."

"You what?" He spun around and faced her.

"Oh, I put everything back," she said quickly, "but I sort of piled up your things in one end of the room . . ."

"What in thunder are you talking about?" He glowered at her. "You've got no business in my workshop. When I want it cleaned, I'll do it myself." He turned angrily toward the door.

"Wait! I've got to tell you something. I thought you wouldn't be using it much this summer, and I have to have a place to raise my chickens . . ."

"Chickens!" Dux exploded. "You must be kidding! You didn't actually imagine I'd let you raise chickens in my tool shed, for gosh sake. You do get the most damnable ideas!"

Panic began to fill Mother's voice as she persisted, "But they're just baby chicks, and it's only for a few months, and you're too busy with pipelines to use it much anyway . . ."

"Chubby, you listen to me." He pointed the stem of his pipe at her. "I'd do most anything for you, but I'll be damned if I'll let you raise chickens in my workshop! You'd better put a bridle on that imagination of yours."

"But, Dux, I've already made a down payment on the brooders and ordered the chicks." Her voice came out high-pitched and tears filled her eyes. "Oh, whatever will I do?"

"Cancel the damn orders! That's what you can do."

"Oh, Dux." Mother sat down in a nearby chair

with her head down. "I don't have much of a life anymore, and I just thought you wouldn't mind." She looked up at him with tears streaming down her face. "I only thought raising chickens would give me an interest and help me earn some money."

"Cancel your agreement, and I mean just that!" he shouted and stared at her as if she were a child he'd like to spank. "You had no business rushing into a thing like this without consulting me. I will not have any gol-derned fowls cluttering up my tool house. And that's final!"

The door slammed behind him as he stomped out of the house.

17

Brooding Over the Brooders

It wasn't too long before big-hearted Dux succumbed to Mother's "molasses." In spite of his brute determination, he turned to putty in the hands of an emotional female. The brooder stoves arrived late Saturday afternoon, and Dux promised Mother he'd help her set them up the next morning.

After breakfast on Sunday, he passed me in the kitchen grumbling about "her velvet paws with the brass knuckles." As he left the house, his compressed lips and the irritated scowl on his face told me he was far from happy about Mother's new project.

Dux had endured a lot with good grace, and my heart hurt with the weight of my love for him. Our lives aren't our own anymore, I thought; everything revolves around Mother. If I'd been smart, I could have stopped the whole thing before it started, but now the chicks were to arrive in four days—all five hundred of them!

Dux told Ginger he'd take her fishing as soon as he got the brooders set up. "You get the rods and reels and see to the fuel in the outboard," he said. "I'll only be a short while."

But at noon, he and Mother were still in the tool shed. Either Mother didn't know as much as she thought she did or the brooder people had left a page out of their directions. Apparently Dux was stumped.

I called them to lunch and we ate sandwiches in silence. Mother kept her eyes on her plate, and the expression on Dux's face reminded me of the sky when a storm is brewing.

Hesitantly I suggested that I telephone the hatchery man and ask him to come out. Mr. Webster, who owned the grocery store eight miles down the road, was very agreeable about letting us use his phone.

"No!" Dux snapped at me. "By thunder, I'll get these dang brooders fixed somehow, but how in hell I ever got hitched into this blasted mess is beyond me."

Right after lunch, they went back to the tool shed.

About three o'clock in the afternoon Ginger gave up waiting for Dux and went fishing by herself. I decided to bake a chocolate cake, Dux's favorite, and to have hickory-smoked country ham, which he dearly loved, for dinner.

At six that night, Mother and Dux both came in looking exhausted. Mother went straight to her room, and Dux collapsed on the couch in the living room. I wanted to tell him how sorry I was, but felt that this was one time he didn't want sympathy.

Here was a man who'd never let any problem lick him. He'd put out dangerous oil and gas fires; he'd tamed wild oil and gas wells; he'd even built pipelines over mountains and across hazardous rivers. But, incredible as it seemed, he had met his Waterloo in two second-hand brooder stoves!

While Ginger and I were doing the dishes after dinner, Mother came into the kitchen, shaking her head despairingly. "I've got so much invested in those baby chicks." She spoke anxiously. "If we can't get these stoves ready for them—well, you can just cash my bonds and hand me over to Gabriel."

Early Monday morning, Dux sent Ginger to the store to phone his office. "Tell them I won't be in today, but I'll try to make it tomorrow."

Ginger snickered, buttoning up her raincoat before facing the damp, cold wind. "If they ask why, should I say you're brooding over the brooders, Dad?"

He scowled at her and angrily gave his pants a hitch at the waist. "They won't ask why, but if they should, tell them it's none of their dad-blasted business. Don't you dare tell anyone what I'm doing!" Completely oblivious of the drizzling rain, he turned and marched out the kitchen door.

Before Ginger left, I told her to call the Sterling Hatchery and ask to have someone come and help get the brooder stoves to work. "But be sure to tell them please not to say who called. He can just stop by casually."

A short time later, I was shredding cabbage for cole slaw when I looked out to see a truck pulling up. Goodness, I thought, the hatchery didn't waste any time. Sterling was twenty-five miles away, and Ginger wasn't back yet from the telephone. I wiped my hands on my apron and went to the door as the truck came to a stop.

"Oh, no!" I groaned. "It can't be!" But it was. The baby chicks had arrived. I opened the door and yelled to Dux and Mother who came running, but when

they saw the cardboard cartons with the round peep-
holes and heard the wild clamor of chirps, they stopped
dead in their tracks.

Mother's hand flew to her throat. "They weren't to
come until Wednesday!" she cried. "He promised me."

Dux tried in vain to get the driver to take them
back, but completely ignoring him, he started swinging
the boxes to the ground.

"Can't nohow," he bellowed above the racket. "I
got to go clear up to Roscommon to get a load of feed."

"We can't leave them here." Mother said frantically. "They've got to be kept warm or they'll die."
She tried to lift a carton, but Dux brushed her aside
and began carrying the boxes up on the porch, the
chicks squawking their protests as if they were being
murdered instead of saved.

As the driver put the last box on the ground, I
walked up to him. "Could you . . . I mean, would you
. . . take a second to look at the brooders?"

He looked down his nose at me. "Lady, I'm just a
truck driver. Don't know nothin' about brooders. Get
a man from the hatchery," he snapped.

Too bewildered to move, I watched him climb
back into the cab and drive away. In a few moments, I
turned around and saw Mother open one of the boxes
on the porch and lift a few of the yelping chicks into
her apron. A couple of the more rambunctious ones
got away and tumbled out the door which Dux had
propped open. Simultaneously Mother yelled for help
and I tried to catch them, but Dux beat me to it and,
with a wild grab, scooped the chickens up in his hands.

"Oh, do be careful," Mother wailed, "if you
squeeze them, they'll die!"

"Well, that's one way of getting out of this damn
mess!" he answered grimly, dropping the culprits into
her apron. "Don't think I'm not tempted, Chubby."

With that, he went back to the tool shed and

worked feverishly through the dreary darkness of the cold, miserable day.

Ginger returned from the phone, took one look at our predicament and burst out laughing. When she recovered, she broke the awful news that they were short-handed at the hatchery, but that they would send out a man if they could.

In the ghastly hours that followed, we were really put to an exhausting test. The business of trying to keep five hundred baby chicks warm and dry taxed our resources and ingenuity to the limit. Mother suggested heating coarse salt in bags to put around them, but we didn't know where to get the salt. Ginger rummaged in a catch-all closet that the previous owners hadn't cleaned, but couldn't find anything useful.

As usual, it took Dux to solve the problem. He brought in bricks and heated them in the fireplace. Then, wrapping them in whatever we could find, including our towels and bed linens, we placed them under the boxes of the excited chickens. The ones that had gotten wet were put inside the oven to dry out.

"Maybe we'd better turn the house over to these smelly loud-mouths and go live in the tool shed," I said, shuddering at the thought.

There were squawking babies all over the place, and we wished for the peace and quiet of the tool shed. The chickens required constant vigil and attention; they had to be fed and watered, and the ones in the oven had to be watched; the bricks couldn't be too hot nor allowed to get cold, so we were continually changing them.

For once, Mother was thoroughly disconcerted, pacing back and forth from one box to another, clucking like a distracted hen. But regardless of her concern, some of the dumb things died, mostly from sheer stupidity—pecking one another's eyes out or

crowding so close they smothered to death. Mother wept over each casualty, and I don't believe she was thinking entirely of the cost.

The rain was coming down in buckets, and it was getting much colder outside, while in the house, the heat and the nauseating odor became oppressive. No one said much, but we couldn't be heard anyway with all the noise. No one was hungry either. Even if I'd taken time out to fix food, we couldn't have eaten it with that smell in our nostrils. We were all tired, but didn't dare relax our routine throughout the night.

At daybreak, Dux grabbed his coat. "I'm going in to Sterling. I'll get that man if I have to yank him out of bed! Keep piling logs on the fire," he said and stalked out the back door.

Two hours later, I heard a car and saw Dux and a man enter the tool shed. My relief was so great that when I tried to yell to Mother and Ginger, my voice simply wouldn't cooperate. Oh, golly, I thought, we're finally going to get these pesky creatures out of the house.

A few minutes later I ran to the door as Dux came in from the tool shed and I saw our car pull away.

"No wonder I couldn't make those darn things work," he said with a wide grin of relief. "They forgot to send the thermostatic wafers—the most important part of the heat control, and the man's gone back to get them."

By noon, the last of the chickens were out of the house, but the reminders lingered on. In spite of the strong disinfectants, hard scrubbing, and even with the cold air blowing through the rooms while we wore sweaters and coats, we still smelled those little stinkers for days.

Sunday, when I put Ginger on the bus for Jackson, I told her how sorry I was that the week had been so hectic. Maybe next summer we would be able to add an extra bedroom so she could bring a friend up with her.

Mother spent endless hours with her project: getting up at dawn to measure feed, keeping an eye on the heat control, fighting parasites, trying different cures for such diseases as pullorum and paralysis. She did everything she could to keep the chicks alive, but they were such stupid things—some of them drowned from sticking their heads too far under the water when they were drinking.

For weeks Mother worried about her chickens, and I worried about her. Many nights I'd lain awake wondering how we could get her out of this mess. We shouldn't have let her get started in the first place, but now I didn't know what to do to help the situation.

She looked both eager and apprehensive, and it didn't take any great perception to see that she regretted her impulse to raise chickens. I wished she'd learned to control her wild ideas and would consult us before getting involved in anything else.

One Saturday morning, Dux and I were finishing breakfast when he looked out the window. "Here comes Chubby," he said. "She looks completely worn out. We ought to put a stop to this nonsense right now."

"I agree, Dux, but what can we do? I've spent many a sleepless night while you've been gone trying to figure it out."

"Let me handle her," he answered confidently. "I'll talk some sense into that overzealous head of hers."

After an hour of arguing, Mother accepted Dux's suggestion of hiring Jeff, a neighboring farm boy, to do the heavy cleaning. At first, she protested the extra expense, but finally gave in, saying, "You keep track of his time, and I'll pay you every penny back out of my profits."

By the last of June, the chickens were ready for market. Unfortunately, it was not a good year for fryers, and we knew the price would be low. Mother watched helplessly while Jeff loaded the squawking things into his father's truck and took them to Bay City.

As I saw Mother slowly climb the steps to the porch, I had a hard battle suppressing my urge to rush out and hug her, but I knew there was nothing I could do to remove her feelings of disappointment and failure.

In the late afternoon, I saw Jeff pull up in his truck and hand Dux a pink slip of paper. After a few moments, Dux bounded up the porch steps, excitedly calling for Mother.

"Here's your hard-earned money, Chubby. You deserve every penny of it. You take it easy from now on and have a good long rest."

She looked at the check, then at Dux, her hands folding and unfolding the slip of paper. "I'm sorry. You were right, of course. I never should have tried to raise chickens. You're so patient—I wonder how you put up with me." Two big tears rolled down her cheeks. "I don't think I even made enough to pay you for Jeff's help."

Dux put his arm around her. "Don't you worry about that, Chubby. It won't bankrupt us, and besides, we need you more than those chickens did."

Mother told me later, "It hurts to owe money, even to Dux, as generous as he is, but somehow I'm going to pay him back."

That night I repeated her words to Dux. "She's fretting because things didn't pan out the way she expected, and she's worried about her debt to you. As far as I'm concerned, it's worth every cent to get her out of such a messy venture."

"Never mind, honey." He smiled to himself. "I'll fix Chubby so she won't be upset anymore."

I was getting breakfast the next morning while Dux was listening to the news. Germany's invasion of Russia brought great concern to our country, and the newscasters were predicting the U.S.S.R. would soon fall into Nazi hands. Our problems with Mother seemed small compared to what Europe was suffering. All we needed was a better perspective!

After we finished eating, Dux asked Mother to get her books so they could go over the accounts. Reluctantly she spread the records on the kitchen table and sat quietly, her eyes on the items in each column while Dux made tiny figures in the margin. She seemed to be holding her breath.

Finally he tossed the pencil on the table and took out his pipe. "You know, Chubby, there are certain fundamental factors in any business enterprise. Now, in breaking down your cost of production: price of chicks, amount of feed per bird, labor, depreciation, the minimized overhead, and taking into consideration the fact that it was your first year in business, I'd say you did pretty well."

"I did?" Mother gasped. "Why, I thought . . ."

"You see," he broke in, holding a match to his pipe, "from a business standpoint, some of the larger items should be capitalized instead of expensed." Then between puffs, he started a long rigamarole of technical accounting terms, talking as if he loved the sound of his own voice. I'm sure Mother didn't understand a thing he said.

"Counting the fryers we ate," he continued, "and the work Jeff did for me, you don't owe me anything. The sale of the brooders will bring in something, too." He got up, knocked his pipe carefully against the big pottery saucer on the table, winked at me and went outside.

For a moment, Mother didn't move. She watched Dux until he made his dramatic exit and the door closed behind him. Then she turned to me, her eyes wet, but with a smile of relief on her face.

"Land o' Goshen! Dux is the most wonderful businessman alive."

18

Invitation To Charm

Ginger had decided to go to Bennington College, and we closed Sandy Cove before Labor Day to go back to Jackson and help her get ready. After a busy week of shopping and packing, we put her on the train for Vermont, along with her steamer trunk, two suitcases and all the paraphernalia a college freshman owns. I had dreaded to see this day come, for my "baby" had been such a joy to me and I knew I'd miss her terribly.

In the lonely days that followed, Mother missed Ginger, too. Sometimes I felt that a good mother and grandmother talk about her would be the next best thing to having her here, but it didn't work out that way. For one thing, Mother had her doubts about the wisdom of a young girl living so far from her family. Nothing I said about the propriety of the college and their rules and regulations convinced her. Modern girls were given way too much freedom and danger lurked everywhere. A word to the wise might not be sufficient—it was better to use a hundred words and say them over and over.

Every day at mail time, Mother came downstairs to watch for the postman. Ginger was usually good about writing and gave glowing accounts of the happenings at Bennington and some of her dates.

"I hope the child won't fall in love with a 'wolf in sheep's clothing,'" Mother said, after reading one of her letters.

I smiled. "You don't have to worry about our Ginger, Mother. Her head may be in the clouds, but her feet are planted firmly on the ground."

Knowing that this was Mother's way, I should have been able to take it in stride, but these were tense, worrisome times quite apart from my missing Ginger. The United States was heading toward war. Young men were already being drafted, and every bit of war news carried with it the implication that our own country would soon be involved. It was painful to read the papers or listen to the news on the radio, but it was impossible not to do so.

Russ was, of course, the most likely target for early drafting, but this promised to be a war that would need every able-bodied man, even those with small children, and that included Bud and Jim. Even Dux, who loved to fly, was still a Captain in the Air Corps Reserve, and I wasn't sure they wouldn't want him also.

He had given up flying when the children were small because it worried me, but now our company had grown to a point where a plane was almost a necessity. Most of his days were spent flying from job to job, while at night he was either on the telephone or trying to catch up with the office work.

Because of this, Mother and I were often alone in the evenings. Sometimes we'd go to a movie or I'd invite friends in for a visit, but most of Mother's time was spent making Christmas presents for the family and crocheting on my tablecloth. It made me dizzy to constantly watch the rhythmic bobbing of the crochet hook in her small, quick hands.

"Don't your fingers ever get tired or numb?" I asked one night as I snipped the thread from the last button I'd finished sewing on Dux's shirt.

"Well, sometimes," she admitted, "but when they do, I stop for awhile."

"Mother, you work too hard," I scolded, marveling at the many millions of loving stitches those nimble fingers had produced.

"You haven't heard me complain, have you?"

"No, I never have." It was true. Mother never complained about work. She wouldn't even admit to being tired, and when anyone asked her how she felt, she always answered, "Just fine."

But what was wrong with her? Only a few months earlier she had been full of pep, happy with our friends, even willing to go visiting. Now she had gone back to the protection of her room, the radio serials and the endless crocheting.

As she sat quietly in the overstuffed chair in the living room, I took a long look at her, trying to be objective. She was wearing one of the dresses she had taken on her trip to Kentucky, but even though it had been let out at the seams, it was still too tight across the midriff. Was it possible that the moodiness and lethargy which were keeping Mother in her room so much of the time were less the result of war news or missing Ginger than of plain boredom and excess weight? Although she had gained some during the frustrating chicken-raising episode, she hadn't referred to it and didn't seem to care. I wondered if she would ever resume her diet and exercises.

Suddenly an idea came to me. "I think you need a change of pace," I told her. "I've been meaning to give a party for you ever since you learned to play canasta, but between the chickens and getting Ginger off to school, there wasn't time. Let's have a luncheon. We can make out a list right now." I walked over to the secretary and picked up a pad and pencil.

"I don't know, Winalee," Mother said hesitantly. "Most likely I've forgotten how to play canasta, and . . . anyway . . . I'm not good enough for those women who play all the time. Besides, don't they play for money?"

"I suppose so, but they won't play for money here. We'll have a prize for the winner. Now let's see," I said, starting to write down some names, "we can invite . . ."

"Couldn't we put it off . . . please . . ." Mother interrupted, "say until after Christmas? That'll give me time to brush up on the game and to finish my presents."

Anything for an excuse, I thought. She had told me most of the gifts were done and Christmas was still weeks away. Was it possible that she had retrograded, not only in her weight but also in her prejudice against cards? I recalled Ginger telling me last winter: "Mam-ma's conscience is still bothering her, but I think she keeps playing just to please you."

Remembering this, I felt a wave of guilt, immediately followed by resentment. I was tired of blaming myself for Mother's problems—it was both confusing and humiliating.

I tore off the page of names and put the pad down on the end table, determined never to bring up the matter of a card party again. As Mother so often said, "You can lead a horse to water . . ."

Before anything else could be said, the front

doorbell rang and I was grateful for the reprieve. I hurried to the door, thinking it might be Dux and he'd been locked out. Instead, it was a special delivery letter for Mother. When I signed the slip, I noticed it was postmarked "New York" and the return address said "Milady's Charm School."

"It's for you, Mother." I waited expectantly while she tore open the envelope and read for a few moments.

"Land o' mercy!" she exclaimed. "Read this."

"My Dear Mrs. Baldwin:

Mr. Gentry has brought to my attention that through your untiring efforts and splendid example, you have inspired fifteen Kentucky ladies to participate in Milady's Correspondence Charm Course.

It is my extreme pleasure to inform you that our Board of Directors has voted to extend to you an invitation to attend our Milady's Charm School. This six-week session will begin on Monday, February 2 in our New York salon.

You will be the very first great-grandmother to be enrolled in this school, and it is our hope that you will be the shining example for others like yourself.

Enclosed please find a schedule and application. Kindly fill out the necessary information and return to us at your earliest convenience.

If I can be of further assistance, please advise.

Very truly yours,

J. Morgan Wadsworth

J. Morgan Wadsworth
President"

"Oh, Mother, that's marvelous!" I hugged her. "Just imagine! Six whole weeks in their salon for free."

"Wasn't it thoughtful of Dux to write the president?" There was a radiant smile on her face. "Really, I didn't do so much for those women in West Liberty—we all did it together."

"But you were the one to get them started," I reminded her, "and the school is grateful to you."

Her expression suddenly became serious. "I feel like a traitor though. I'll bet I'm the only one to backslide. I not only didn't finish the lessons, but I skipped *Roll Your Own* on those new-fangled curlers and *How to Tango*." She turned to me with a forlorn look on her face. "I'd hate to have the girls find it out."

"Don't you worry, Mother. Now you'll be able to take off more pounds and learn so many new things," I assured her, "and from experts, too, right on exclusive Fifth Avenue."

"What?" Mother asked incredulously. "You don't think I'm actually going all the way to New York, do you? Why, that's ridiculous!"

"For heavens sake, why not? It's free."

"Fiddlesticks! For one thing, I'm too old to go

traipsing all over, and for another, it's not free. They don't pay for a room, and they don't pay for food either."

"But, Mother . . ."

"They've got an axe to grind, that's all." I must have looked puzzled, for she picked up the letter and handed it to me. "Read that paragraph," she said, pointing to one part with her finger.

"It says you'll be the very first great-grandmother to be enrolled, and they hope your example will pave the way for others." I finished reading and gave it back to her. "So what? You'll be a good ad for them. They've got to have something for the money they're going to spend on you."

Mother tossed her head. "I will not be an advertisement for anybody, and that's final." She folded the letter and put it back in the envelope.

Her flat statement gave me a cold chill. It simply had not occurred to me that she would refuse. Knowing how much she liked the correspondence course, I had assumed she'd jump at the chance to take it first hand.

"So you're going to turn it down," I said in stunned disbelief. "You're going to be stubborn and throw away this wonderful opportunity, all because you're afraid you might be exploited!"

Mother put down her crocheting and looked at me over her spectacles. Her eyes were stern. "Do you think I'd let them make a cat's paw out of me?"

"Oh, you're being silly," I scolded and got up to leave the room. "I'm going to bed," I said, thoroughly disgusted.

Before I fell asleep that night I wondered what earthly good it did me to be perpetually concerned about Mother. Why couldn't I just tell myself that we were providing for her physically and would do what we could for her socially, then all of us go about our

own activities? Why did I still behave like some Sweet
Alice, all nerves and guilt because I couldn't accomplish
the impossible? Goodness knows, there was plenty to
keep me busy without stewing about Mother and how
she spent her time and whether it made her happy or
not. Ha! But I knew I was only fooling myself when I
thought this way; I could no more break my bond with
her or be indifferent to her than I could with my own
children.

For the next few days, the charm course was the
main topic of conversation in our house. Dux said it
seemed like a good idea to him, but Mother was
unyielding.

At dinner one night, I said, "Golly! Being in New
York for six whole weeks would surely be an
adventure for me. I simply can't imagine anyone
turning it down."

Mother looked at me and said in a flat voice,
"You're so anxious for me to go. Could it be that you
want to get rid of me for awhile?"

"Oh, Mother!" I banged the table in disgust. "You
make me furious. You know that's not true."

"Now, girls!" Dux interrupted. "Chubby, we're
really only thinking of you, but if you don't want to go,
that's your prerogative."

On Sunday, Mother came down to breakfast
smiling contentedly, and I wondered what sort of a
surprise she would spring on us this time. I was just
starting to pour the coffee and waited for her to speak.

"You know, I've been doing a lot of thinking."
Looking intently at me to catch my reaction, she
continued, "I've changed my mind and filled out the
application. I've decided to go to New York."

135

19

Troubled Christmas

That Sunday turned out to be a day which America would remember with horror—December 7, 1941—Pearl Harbor Day! Shocked to numbness, we huddled close to the radio all afternoon and far into the night. We had been disturbed enough over the war in Europe, but the surprise bombing of our naval base and the killing of so many of our men was a staggering blow. President Roosevelt was calling an emergency session of Congress to declare war on Japan.

Martha was off that day, so I made a big pot of coffee and put bread, butter, cheese and ham on the table for friends who dropped by, but we had little appetite for food. It was well past midnight when we finally went to bed.

"I never thought I'd live to see another war," Mother's voice faded to a whisper as I tucked her into bed, "but I reckon 'what can't be cured must be endured.'"

I kissed her good night. "Try to go to sleep and not worry about it, Mother. There isn't anything we can do but pray."

"Oh, no, Winalee, you're wrong. We can all put our shoulders to the wheel. There'll be a lot of work to do. War is an awful thing, but as long as there's greed, there'll be trouble."

"That's true." I started to leave the room, anxious for her to get some rest.

"Winalee, I'll get a letter off to that school tomorrow."

Puzzled, I turned around. "We mailed it this morning, don't you remember?"

"Of course, I remember, but you don't think I'm going to New York now! Every man and every woman will be needed. War isn't just waving flags and singing 'God Bless America'—it's rolling bandages, knitting sweaters, socks and mittens. My waistline doesn't matter with so many more important things to be done."

"Mother, it isn't only your waistline, it's your heart and your health."

"Fiddlesticks!" she broke in. "There's not a thing wrong with me. I'm as strong as a horse."

But even war and her do-or-die spirit wouldn't keep Dr. Lewis's warning from ringing in my ears. I couldn't add to my mother's life span, but I surely could keep her from subtracting years on earth.

"Look, Mother, there'll probably be a list of volunteers a mile long, and my name will be on it. You certainly did your share in the last war, so why don't you leave this one to the younger generation?" The second the words left my mouth, I knew I'd made a mistake, and I could have bitten my tongue.

She sat up quickly. "Well, if I'm too old for any

use, why bother about a little fat? Just shoot me and be done with it! Old Gabriel is waiting for me anyhow."

Ineptly I tried to apologize, but my words were halting and ineffective. I made a few remarks about things looking brighter in the morning, but we both knew it was like whistling in the dark, and I finally left the room completely exhausted.

Saturday's mail brought a letter from the Barbizon Hotel in answer to my request for reservations for Mother. Hastily I shoved it into the pocket of my housecoat to prevent her from seeing it.

"Is that a letter from Ginger you got?"

Realizing I should have known better than to try to hide anything from her sharp eyes, I gave it to her and said I'd write them at once to forget it.

I went down to the basement to check through the boxes of Christmas decorations. Life had to go on in spite of war and turmoil, and we wanted everything to be as normal as possible for Ginger's holiday vacation. While I was testing the tiny red and green tree lights, Mother came down the steps. She pulled a chair over and sat down beside me.

"Winalee, that letter you got from the New York hotel—did you know it's a place just for women?"

"Of course." What earthly difference did that make, I wondered crossly since she'd made up her mind not to go anyway, but I swallowed my annoyance and said, "It's a good location, fairly quiet and well recommended."

"I've been thinking . . ." She stopped, picked up a ceramic Santa Claus out of the box and began wiping the dust off with her handkerchief. "I don't really think the location matters too much, and I never did mind the noise." She dropped the Santa back into the box and stood up, looking at me with her quick, urchin grin. "For mercy's sake, if I'm going to spend six weeks in a place, I want to see a pair of pants once in a while!"

I dropped the light bulbs in my lap and let out a gasp. "Oh, Mother! You are absolutely the limit. You've really decided to go?"

"Well, as Dux said, I can knit in my spare time there as well as here and he's right, but you've got to promise me one thing—I want to go to the lake early. It looks as if this old war is going to last a spell, and I can still do my bit."

"Oh, golly! Chickens again?"

"What's wrong with chickens?" Mother asked defensively. "Dux said I did all right considering it was my first year." Then she paused and I held my breath. "No, I'm through with fowls. This summer I want to grow vegetables."

"That's a good idea!" I felt relieved that this was something we could handle. "There's a leftover roll of chicken wire we can use to fence off a patch against the rabbits, but you can't plant most things up there until the middle of May because the nights are too cold."

"I know that, but I can start some seeds in the basement here. Then, when we go to Sandy Cove, they'll be ready for transplanting. I'll write Jeff and see if he'll go over and plow up a patch when the ground thaws."

She has it all worked out, I thought. It would definitely take a bit of doing to keep ahead of my ingenious mother!

The weekend before Christmas, we put up all our decorations and trimmed the tree. Mother brought her handmade gifts and put them under it—gifts that were wrapped in last year's Christmas paper and tied with carefully pressed ribbons.

This would probably be our last family get-together for some time. Dux and I weren't happy knowing that Bud wanted to enlist, but Mother was panic-stricken at the thought of unmarried Russ being drafted immediately. The only bright spot was our hope that Jim would be deferred because his automotive plant was scheduled to convert to defense work.

Every time the war was mentioned, Ginger acted as though she felt guilty because she wasn't doing anything to help. Maybe it was the fact that they were already having air raid drills and practice black-outs in the East that made her so war-conscious.

Christmas Day was a joyous one for all of us, but it was over far too quickly. Mother, Dux and I rehearsed our happy memories over a late supper that evening. We giggled as Dux again gave his peculiar Santa Claus laugh, remembering Jimmy's delighted squeals and Hoddy's anguished screams.

"Mother, you were really the one who stole the show though," I told her, taking a bite out of my turkey sandwich.

"Yes, Chubby," Dux agreed. "When you strutted across the room in the blue negligee we gave you and everyone could see 'Old Ironsides' under it, I thought I'd split my seams with laughter!" He took a sip of coffee, then added, "That's one thing I hope New York will change!"

20

Chubby's Rejuvenation

Although I was happy that Mother was going to New York, I was a bit uneasy when we put her on the train and waved good-bye. To travel alone to an unfamiliar place and to face strangers in an entirely new experience took a lot of courage on her part.

"Dux, do you think Mother will be lonely in such a big city?" I asked as we were walking back to the car.

"Chubby'll get along just fine," he said reassuringly. "When she wants to, she can adapt to anything. Before you know it, she'll have a flock of friends."

"That's true," I said, beginning to feel better. "The people she meets won't remain strangers for long." I squeezed his hand acknowledging my thanks.

Two nights later we were at dinner when the

telephone rang. I heard Martha answer, but couldn't distinguish her words. Disliking to have Dux disturbed at mealtime, I had instructed her to take the message or ask the caller to phone back later—unless, of course, it was an emergency.

Suddenly Martha burst into the dining room, wringing her hands. "It's Miz Baldwin, the poor lamb. They're puttin' her out of that place."

"What?" I ran to the phone, and Dux hit the stairs two at a time to reach the extension.

"Mother, what is it? What's happened?" I cried.

"Oh, Winalee! I hated to call you long distance. I know it costs money, but I didn't know what else to do." Her voice trembled. "I was never so mortified in my whole life. That doctor . . ."

"Mother, are you all right?" My hands clenched the receiver.

"Yes, I'm fine." The sob in her voice belied her words. "Except I'm so mad I could burst! I just wish I were a man for five minutes. I'd show that old sawbones . . ."

"Get to the point, Chubby," Dux put in quickly.

"Oh, hi, Dux. Well, this doctor, the old whipper-snapper, told me I couldn't take the course. He wouldn't even talk to me after I'd stood in line over twenty minutes. Said he didn't have time to argue, but they gave me this course, and I told him so, only he wouldn't listen. Then I went to the head of the school and she was nice, but she said the doctor had the last word, and there wasn't anything she could do. They'd already taken my picture and my measurements and given me all the instructions, but they wouldn't let me start in the class and . . ." She broke off.

"Golly, Mother, I'm so sorry . . ." I began.

Dux interrupted. "Why did they turn you down?"

"I thought I told you. It's high blood pressure,

and I tried to tell him it's only because I'm too fat, and that's why I'm here. He refused to listen to me. I've never been treated so . . ."

"Did he tell you what it was? I mean your blood pressure—is it higher than it was before?" Dux persisted.

"I don't know. He wouldn't even talk to me—just yelled, 'Next.' All the others heard how rude he was, and they said it was a shame." We could hear her blowing her nose.

"Now you listen carefully," Dux began patiently. "Tomorrow you call Dr. Franklin Seward who is a friend of ours. He's an optometrist in the Empire State Building and would be listed in the Yellow Pages. He knows many of the physicians in New York. Ask him to recommend a good one for you, then have this doctor give you a thorough physical examination. Afterwards, tell him your problem, and if he agrees with the school doctor, there's nothing you can do. If not, ask him to contact the school for you and see if they'll take you back on his recommendation. Got it?"

"Oh, yes!" Eagerness warmed Mother's voice. "I just don't know what I'd do without you and Winalee. I know I ought to hang up, but I want you to know what a comfort you are to me, Dux."

What a comfort he is to me, too, I thought. I'd been so stunned at Mother's first words I couldn't even think straight. It was such a relief to have someone else take over.

"And use your head, Chubby," he was saying. "It's not good for you to get steamed up. Go to bed early, get a good night's sleep, and call us when you get the verdict. Make it collect. I'll have the charges reversed on this call."

Martha had been standing at my elbow, twisting the corner of her apron. When I hung up, she said, "Is she gonna stay? Don't you let 'em put her out, Miz

Gentry!"

"We won't if we can help it," I assured her. Feeling a bit weary, I went back into the dining room.

Dux came in with a big smile on his face. "Whatever did we do for excitement before Chubby came?"

There was no humor in the situation for me. "I wish I could be with her," I murmured. "She hates going to a doctor alone and even more having a physical."

"Stop worrying, honey. Our Chubby is quite a character. I'll bet a dollar she comes through with flying colors."

The depressed feeling was still with me when I awoke the next morning. I lay thinking about Mother's problem—then remembered suddenly that it was Martha's day off. I grabbed my housecoat and hurried downstairs to start the coffee before waking Dux.

It was not a day for feeling droopy. Bright sunshine flooded the warm kitchen, and Jack Frost had painted a picture on the window over the sink. I looked out at the glistening snow, wondering if it were cold in New York or if Mother would have trouble getting a taxi.

I wanted to keep busy every minute of the hours ahead, but as the day wore on, my uneasiness grew. I cleaned cupboards, made a ham loaf and even baked an angel food cake from Mother's old recipe, but I got to crying in the middle of it. When I took the cake from the oven, it fell and we were both a mess.

Dux came home around six. "Heard from Chubby?"

I shook my head.

"It might take a day or two to get an appointment with a busy physician, but I'm positive everything is going to be okay," he assured me confidently.

Twenty minutes later the phone rang.

"Have I ever been through the wringer today!" There was a lilt in Mother's voice that took a load off my shoulders. "Dr. Seward is so nice. He made an appointment with this doctor—I can't pronounce his name, but he's wonderful. He said he wished he had more patients like me."

"Come on, Chubby," Dux put in from the extension. "What's the verdict?"

"Well, this doctor called the school, and I heard every word he said and I was so proud, but he did say I wasn't to have heavy exercises. I can have a massage every day, though, and you know, that bothers me. I never had a massage in my life. Did you know they put you on a table as naked as the day you were born?"

"Look, Chubby," Dux answered. "You haven't got anything different from any other female—you've simply got more of it."

"I know that, but . . ."

"Mother, don't be such an old fogy," I cut in. "There isn't anything indecent about a massage. Just be thankful your school has a masseuse instead of a masseur—that's a man."

She gasped. "You don't mean that a man would actually give a massage to a woman? Well, I never!" I could imagine the color rising in her plump cheeks.

Dux laughed. "Chubby, haven't you realized that you are living in a dangerous age? This is a man's world."

"Don't let any prudish ideas bother you," I told her. "It isn't any different than having a doctor or a nurse."

"Well, I think it is," she said firmly, "but I'll do it if it kills me, and most likely it will! We'd better hang up. I don't believe in wasting money. I'll write you."

"You take care of yourself. Try not to be

lonesome," I said.

"Oh, I won't be. Everyone is so nice. Even the taxi driver opened the door of his cab and walked me to the doctor's office. He said his wife's mother lives with them and she complains all the time. I told him to find something for her to do, and he said he'd already tried, but she just grumbled, and he wished she had my get-up-and-go." She cleared her throat and added, "We've simply got to hang up. 'A penny saved is a penny earned,' don't forget."

I put the receiver on the hook. When Dux came downstairs, I said, "I hope that taxi man turned off his meter when he was telling Mother the story of his life."

"Just like I said, Chubby will always find friends," he responded with an 'I told you so' grin. "She's genuinely interested in people, so you don't need to worry about her being lonesome, no matter where she is. People like her because she has a way of making them like themselves."

Mother kept us informed of her activities in the charm school. She wrote in her first letter:

"For the first week, our diet is only oranges and mineral oil. That's to clean us out so we start fresh and healthy, like a new-born baby. After this is over, I may want to go to Florida and grow oranges. With the number of fat women in this place and all the oranges they have to eat, it seems to me I could make a lot of money."

The second letter told about the small family hotel she'd found not far from the school and the interesting people who lived there.

"I like my room. It isn't large, but
it's cozy, and I love my bathroom so
much that I seldom stray too far
away from it. I'd like to go sightseeing, but I wouldn't dare. I'm as
weak as a kitten and as well-oiled as
Ma's old sewing machine. In two
more days, I'll be able to lessen the
doses, that is, if there's anything left
of me by then."

I questioned the wisdom of this strenuous therapy,
but finally dismissed these doubts from my mind.
After all, this school had been in business a long time,
and their doctor watched carefully and gave each
student individual attention.

Mother had been in New York ten days when we
received a package containing three pairs of dark
green knitted socks and two wool mufflers for me to
take to the Red Cross. I was glad that she'd had
knitting to keep her busy during the many hours she
was confined to her room. A letter also came that day
with no salutation. It started right out:

"My, oh my, today I ate! Baked
potato, steamed string beans and a
tiny piece of broiled steak. No salt,
no butter, no cream in my coffee,
but if you don't think it tasted like
heaven, you try living on oranges
and mineral oil for seven days. You
have to be really hungry to get the
full enjoyment out of what you eat.
I've changed my mind about growing oranges. Once I get through
here, I never want to look another
orange in the face."

Mother told us about some of her classmates, one
in particular.

"Mrs. Simpson is a widow, and she's
not very pretty although she might
have been before she gained forty-
five pounds and let her hair get
straggly. Her face is so fat her eyes
look pushed up, but that doesn't
give anyone the right to laugh at
her as some people are doing. I'm
beginning to understand why women
are called 'cats.' I never did like the
sly things—cats, I mean."

We watched eagerly for her letters. In fact, the
entire neighborhood was interested in this wholesale
shedding of pounds. Almost every day some friend
would run in or telephone to ask for Mother's latest
news. Even the postman, who had been with us for
years, often lingered to ask, "What's Mrs. Baldwin up
to now?"

I sent most of Mother's letters on to Ginger at
school, and she once wrote, "Mam-ma's escapades have
my roommate in hysterics. She even goes to the mail
desk with me every day, hoping to hear about her."

Mother's next letter told about walking with a
book on her head, listening to lectures on poise and
personality development and learning to do her hair in
a becoming style.

"I never thought I'd ever get the
hang of putting on make-up proper-
ly, but reckon I'm smarter than I
gave myself credit for. I'm learning
the new dance steps, too. You
know, I always did like to dance, but
I couldn't do much good in class, so
the instructor is giving me private
lessons at a special rate because I'm
at this school."

"Now what do you think of that?" I'd been

reading her letter aloud to Dux.

"It sounds like our Chubby is stepping high, wide and handsome, but it's good exercise. When you write her, tell her if she gets it down pat, we'll take her to a dance at the country club when she comes home."

Around the first of March, one of Mother's letters began:

> "Last Saturday, Mrs. Simpson (she's the one everyone used to make fun of) and I went shopping for our graduation bathing suits, and don't you know, I had to pay eighteen dollars for mine! I never dreamed they cost so much. Of course, I haven't bought a bathing suit in twenty years. We got on one of those double-decker buses, and it was such fun sitting on top, freezing and giggling like a pair of schoolgirls. Simpie really is a sweet person once you get to know her, and she can talk in three different languages. It just goes to show, 'you can't judge a book by its cover.' She looks better, too, since she's lost some weight and learned to fix her hair. Those 'cats' aren't laughing now. They're impressed."

Mother wouldn't tell us how many pounds she had lost because she wanted to surprise us.

> "Wait until you see me. You may not even know your old ma with her new figure, new hairdo and a much better complexion. We're all excited over graduation, but I'm just sick that you and Dux can't come. This

has been such a wonderful experience for me that I'm sorry to see it end. I really do feel like a new person, and I want you to know how happy I am."

21

The Star Graduate

"How would you like to drive to New York?" Dux asked me casually.

"Oh, Dux, could we? I can't think of anything more wonderful than to see Mother graduate." I hadn't expected him home from the office so early and was upstairs sewing when he had come in. Tossing my fabric down on the table, I jumped up and threw my arms around him. "What a marvelous surprise!"

"I knew it would make you happy. Since I have a lot of business calls to make in the East, I figured I could combine them with Chubby's graduation. We'll have to leave early tomorrow morning because I want to be in Cleveland by noon. I set up my appointments for the next three days, and we can be in New York on Friday. You get the suitcases packed, and I'll put them in the car tonight."

I immediately wrote Mother the good news and drove to the post office to make sure the letter would go out that evening. Then I told Martha she could have a week off. It did me good to see her wide grin of appreciation.

"Lawsy me, I'm gonna take a bus to see Ozzie," she said, her eyes shining. "He's at the army post in Kalamazoo, and he's been coaxin' me to come see him for weeks."

After dinner, I went to the attic to get our luggage, and by ten o'clock the car was packed so we could leave at daybreak the next morning.

As it turned out, we arrived in New York a bit earlier than we'd expected. I had told Mother it would be close to noon, but when we pulled up to her hotel it was only eleven o'clock.

When we registered, the clerk recognized our name. "So you're the daughter and son-in-law we've heard so much about." He smiled and his welcome made us feel very important. "Mrs. Baldwin isn't here right now, but she left word that . . . oh, here she comes now."

I spun around and stood immobile. It was simply not possible to believe this lovely woman in a trim periwinkle blue suit and pert hat could be my mother. With complete assurance and poise, she walked toward us with the air of one who knows she is looking her best. Her hair, now natural looking auburn, was styled beautifully, complimenting her clear and radiant complexion; her make-up was so expertly done that it made her look far younger than her years; her figure was absolutely amazing. I heard Dux whistle under his breath and whisper "Sacre-bluey!"

"Oh, my goodness! I'm so happy you could come," she exclaimed, her eyes dancing as she kissed us.

Then turning to the clerk, she announced proudly, "My family!"

I simply couldn't stop staring at Mother. A group of people came over and we were introduced and I must have said something, but I mocked myself inside. How could I ever have thought her old? Why, she's younger than I am in many ways—so eager, so full of wonder, laughing with the sheer joy of being alive.

We talked most of the afternoon, and she told us all about the school, the many people she knew and the fun she'd had.

"Mrs. Simpson has invited us to dinner. I hope you won't mind. She's really a nice person, but she's had a pretty hard time," Mother explained sympathetically.

That evening we went to a Parisian restaurant with Mrs. Simpson. I thought she seemed a bit snobbish, always talking to the waiter in French and telling us about the exotic trips she'd taken. Occasionally she would interject foreign words here and there in the conversation so that Dux and I would be impressed.

After we'd said good night to her, I asked Mother how long she'd been a widow.

"Oh, she's not widowed. She just speaks of her husband as though he were dead. He walked out on her a long time ago and I can't blame him, but I do feel sorry for her."

"Why did he leave her? What'd she do?"

"Probably because he couldn't take her avoirdupois!" Dux put in with a flash of humor.

Mother shook her head. "No, Simpie didn't get fat until later. I reckon she just thought she could hold a man with her brain."

"What do you mean?" I asked.

"It's plain simple. Her husband was always mussing up her hair trying to kiss her and she couldn't stand it. Simpie may have a mind for foreign

153

languages, but she sure is dumb about men."

"Did you tell her that, Chubby?" Dux asked facetiously.

"Well, it wasn't any of my business, and anyway it's too late now, but I did say she should have decided what she wanted—a happy husband or a slick hair-do."

The graduation ceremony was set for two-thirty the next day, but we went over right after lunch because I was anxious to see and hear about all the things that had changed Mother so completely. It was no surprise to me that everyone smiled and nodded at her—from the gold-braided doorman to Miss Mayfield, the director of the charm school.

As she guided us through the school, she pointed out the various exercising rooms. Each was devoid of furniture except for the full-length mirror on the wall and a table with an electric phonograph. All the floors were black rubber.

"Most of the exercises are taken lying down," Mother explained. "It's more relaxing that way, and everything is done to music."

The rooms were full of people who had come to see their relatives or friends graduate. Although there were a few men, some in uniform, the visitors were mostly women, and it was usually easy to pick out Mother's classmates from among them.

"Yikes!" Dux said under his breath when Mother brought her teachers over to introduce them. They were quite young, and each had a beautifully proportioned figure that her clothes showed off to its fullest advantage. However, they all had the same glistening wavy hair, in various colors, and exactly the same artificial make-up.

Dux asked Mother about the doctor. "That old whippersnapper, as you called him—I'd like to meet him."

"Oh, he's on vacation, but once I got to know him, he wasn't so bad," she said, springing to his defense. Mother never holds a grudge, I marveled; she always looks for the best in everyone and usually finds it.

A gong sounded and Mother hurried away to get dressed, or rather, undressed, for the performance. We followed the usher to our chairs. The pink walls and indirect lighting in the long salon were soothing and relaxing. Across one end of the room were black velvet draperies which closed off the stage. A picture screen stood to one side.

A hush of anticipation fell over the crowd as a tall, suave gentleman, Mr. J. Morgan Wadsworth, president of the school, stepped up to the microphone to introduce Miss Mayfield. Probably a perennial thirty-nine, she was slender and well-groomed with a lovely voice.

She gave a brief history of the aims and accomplishments of the school, the pride of the instructors in their teaching and the fine reputation Milady's Charm School had earned over the years.

"Now we want to show you what has been done. This is the 'before' picture, taken the day this lady enrolled." A slide flashed on the the small screen, and the audience tittered. "But I'm sure you will appreciate what six weeks of hard work can do when you see her now."

The velvet curtains parted and I recognized Mrs. Simpson. She had so much more to lose than Mother, but she had come a long way, and I'm sure she was gratified by the applause. Miss Mayfield gave her name, her new measurements, and spoke of her grace as she walked across the stage displaying perfect poise.

This went on until Dux became restless and whispered that he thought they'd forgotten Mother.

"They're saving the best until last," I murmured.

Finally it was her turn. When the "before" picture flashed on the screen, Dux roared. It was so funny! The legs of the school bathing suit hung halfway to her knees, and without "Old Ironsides" her stomach protruded about like mine just before Bud was born.

Miss Mayfield was saying, "Mrs. Baldwin is the first great-grandmother to take our course and in the beginning there were many complications, but with characteristic determination, she plunged right in, overcoming all obstacles. She has been an inspiration to each of us and her enthusiasm has been contagious. Now, let us see her as she is today."

Dux squeezed my fingers sensing my emotion.

The curtains parted and there she stood, silhouetted against the dark backdrop in her eighteen dollar blue-flowered silk jersey bathing suit. She stood in profile—chin up, shoulders back and stomach in. There were gasps of admiration on all sides of us. Oh, how I wished Dad could see his "Kewpie doll" now! I whispered to Dux he'd have to find another nickname as Mother was anything but chubby now.

Smiling confidently, she turned and faced us while Miss Mayfield gave her weight and measurements. The expressions on the faces around us paid tribute to this elderly woman who had endured six weeks of training and discipline. As she walked across the stage and back with perfect posture, I could picture her practicing for hours with a book on her head.

Just then, Mr. Wadsworth came up to her carrying an armful of long-stemmed red roses. With starry eyed surprise, she graciously accepted the flowers, stepping back and smiling until the curtain closed. The applause was deafening.

22

Mysterious Suitor

Sunday morning I awakened with the feeling that I had smiled all night. What a wonderful world this would be if it weren't for the war, but at least we wouldn't have to worry about Mother, I thought. She not only had years to live, years that stretched excitingly ahead to do as she pleased, but now her enthusiasm for living was so evident that I was confident these years would bring her satisfying fulfillment.

I slipped out of bed, quietly gathered my clothes and went into the bathroom to dress. Dux was still asleep, but I knew Mother would be up since she was planning to go to Mrs. Simpson's home in Virginia on the eleven o'clock train. Mrs. Simpson's brother was supposed to be a good dancer, and Mother was looking forward to an active time with the two of them.

Hurrying down the hall, I tapped on Mother's door.

"I knew it was you," she greeted me. "Reckon you get your early bird trait from me. I've been up for hours and have already ordered coffee." She scooped clothes off a chair and motioned for me to sit down. Dresses, slips, stockings and filmy underwear were strewn over the bed and chairs. Two suitcases stood open on the luggage racks.

"I'm packing one for you to take home," she said, folding her graduation swim suit in tissue paper and laying it carefully in the larger suitcase.

"Sure you won't need that?" I kidded her.

"Positive. I'm just taking my wool suit, two or three blouses and, of course, my party dress." She held it up in front of her to show me. "You know, the salesgirl called it a 'cocktail' gown. I told her that was silly because everyone doesn't drink those things. She probably thought I was crazy."

"It's just a word to describe an 'after-five' dress," I told her absently. "This Mrs. Simpson's brother—is he a bachelor or widower?"

"His wife died over a year ago, and now he doesn't have any kinfolks left except Simpie."

"Is he older or younger than she is?"

Mother laughed. "He's a bit older than I am. It seems good to be able to say that. There have been times when I thought I was about the oldest person alive, but not anymore. Years don't mean a thing. It's just how you use them that counts—and how you think."

"That's true," I said, overjoyed with Mother's new youthful perspective. "What's her brother's business?" I prodded.

"He's a lawyer. I've seen his picture, and he's good-looking. He lives with Simpie in Virginia, but he's going to meet us at the train station in Washington." Her face flushed, and I wondered what Mrs. Simpson had told her. Should I warn my naive mother about the "wolf in sheep's clothing"? In some ways, she seemed more inexperienced than Ginger.

The coffee came and I poured two cups, dropping a lump of sugar in mine. "Getting back to this lawyer . . ."

"You know," Mother broke in quickly, "I don't even miss sugar and cream. It just goes to show that you can get used to anything, once your mind is made up.

"I've a feeling that your friend is a matchmaker," I persisted, refusing to be sidetracked. "She's trying to find a wife for her brother, isn't she?"

"Oh, pooh!" Mother set her cup on the tray and stood up. "I'd better start getting dressed." She avoided looking at me.

"I bet a dollar she told you that," I blurted out. "That's why she wants you to go home with her so he can look you over. Oh, Mother!"

She looked guilty. "Well, come to think of it, she did mention something like that. Said it would be nice if John did marry again. Simpie wants to live in California, but he keeps telling her she can't leave him alone."

"Ha!" I exclaimed. "It's no wonder she wants to get rid of him. He's selfish. Probably he's one of those egotists who thinks the world revolves around the sex."

Mother looked at me and grinned. "Well, doesn't it?"

The telephone rang and we told Dux we'd meet him downstairs for breakfast.

Shortly after ten, we drove Mother and Mrs. Simpson to Grand Central Station. Dux had bought each of them a gardenia corsage, and they both looked very chic. As we walked to the train, Mother's twinkling eyes and animation caused several people, mostly men, it seemed to me, to turn and look at her. She had an air of suppressed excitement about her, as if adventure were just around the corner. Although I tried not to show my anxiety, I wished that Mother weren't so gullible.

When their train pulled away, I could not help feeling apprehensive. It was like the time I watched our small Buddy trudge down the walk on his first day of school. Early this morning I had thought my problems with her were over, but now I could see other challenges that I'd never dreamed of. What if she did marry Mrs. Simpson's brother? Would she be happy? I could imagine myself worrying more about Mother's romances than I did about Ginger's.

We had been home almost a week when it was time to meet Mother's train at the Jackson depot.

"My, it's good to be here." Mother kissed us. "I always say the best part of any trip is coming home."

She was bright and cheerful, but I couldn't help noticing that every time I asked about Mrs. Simpson's brother she would change the subject.

I waited until bedtime, then went to her room. "Okay, Mother," I demanded. "Come on! Give! Tell me what happened with Mrs. Simpson's brother."

She was setting her hair and turned to look at me with feigned astonishment. "Why, nothing happened. Whatever do you mean?"

"Don't give me that," I said in exasperation. "I want to know what you did, what you said, and everything else. And if you don't tell me, I'm going to keep pestering you until you do."

"Well, we went dancing, and they took me sightseeing, the Smithsonian Institution, Library of Congress, and I wanted to see the inside of the White

House, but visitors aren't allowed during war time."
She rolled her last curl, stuck in a pin and sat down in
her rocker. "My goodness, but Washington was
crowded. Everyone I talked to was so worried about
General MacArthur's troops in Bataan. You know,
Winalee, they hardly have any food or ammunition left.
I saw soldiers and sailors everywhere. It was so sad to
watch them say good-bye to their beloved ones at the
train station, and . . ."

"Mother!" I interupted. "I want to hear about
Mrs. Simpson's brother."

"Well, he's tall," she drawled, "and he's not as
handsome as his picture, and well, I reckon he'd make
some woman a good husband, but . . ."

"But not for you, huh?"

"Oh, I don't really know. I can't help judging men
by your dad, and they all fall short." She got up and
started folding back the spread.

"Just tell me one last thing—did he ask you to
marry him?"

She looked me straight in the eyes, and there was
a frown on her face. "I don't want to talk about it
anymore, Winalee. I'm sleepy. Now you go on and let
me go to bed."

23

The Wallflower Blooms

Mother was sitting in front of her dressing table peering at her face. The door was ajar and when she saw me, she smiled in the mirror.

"You know, Winalee, one thing the cosmetics teacher cautioned us about was rouge. Said to be sure to use it sparingly. Lots of older women wear too much and they look like clowns. I've been wondering if it isn't because they can't see well. Maybe they ought to use a magnifying mirror—that's what we were told to do."

"Aren't you glad you don't have to worry about that, Mother? Your eyes are really good, even though you do wear glasses."

She laughed. "I didn't have time to tell you about the funny thing that happened in New York. I made an appointment with Dr. Seward to have him look at my eyes because I thought my glasses might need changing. He asked me how old I was, but I didn't want to tell him. He just smiled and said I didn't have to. Said he'd tell me after he examined my eyes. Well, he took all kinds of tests and when he was through, don't you know, he thought I was ten years younger than I really am."

"No one would ever guess your age, especially now, but it's good to know you have excellent eyesight." Although she'd worn glasses since I was a child, she could still thread a needle faster than I could.

"The girls will be here around ten," I said. "They're anxious to see you and hear all about your school." Several of my friends were coming over this morning for Mother's "unveiling," and I was eager to show her off.

"Maybe they'd like to see my notebook," she offered. "I put down everything they told us." Suddenly she stood up and added with a twinkle in her eyes, "I might even model my bathing suit!" She started parading around the room with her hips wiggling back and forth like a flirtatious schoolgirl, and she kept it up until I was doubled over with laughter and tears were streaming down my face.

"You don't even look like the same person!" Nellie May exclaimed when Mother met her at the door. Mother playfully curtsied and then ushered her into the living room. "I'm simply astonished," Nellie May said to the other guests. "Mrs. Baldwin has actually dropped years as well as pounds."

Mother had a wonderful time telling them about the exercises, the foods, the weekly examination by the school doctor and many of the amusing things that had happened. The girls were thoroughly enjoying her when Martha came in with a tray of hot coffee and

"Just coffee, thanks, Martha," Mother said politely and the girls all laughed.

"How can you possibly pass up these delicious cookies?" Pris Williams said. "Such will power! I can never ignore sweets."

"Well, I must say I did work hard, but it was worth every bit of it," Mother explained, "and I'm not going to undo everything now. There's nothing I can do about getting old, but there is something I can do about getting fat."

"Come on upstairs," she said when they'd finished eating. "I want you to see my graduation suit and some of my new clothes."

After the girls left, Mother lamented. "Oh, golly! I forgot to tell them about the new dance steps I've learned."

"By the way, that reminds me. Next Saturday night there's a dance at the country club given for the Red Cross. Dux and I thought perhaps you'd like to go with us."

"Oh, I'd love it, and now I can wear my new party dress." Then with a sigh, she added, "I'm glad we can help the Red Cross, but how I wish this old war would end."

What fun it would be to introduce Mother to all our friends! Some had met her before she'd lost weight, and I smiled to myself thinking of their surprise.

While Dux was still fussing with his dress studs, I went into Mother's bedroom expecting to zip her up, but I was too late; she was already completely dressed.

"You look lovely," I told her, admiring the turquoise blue cocktail gown which so beautifully accentuated her new slim figure. The long lines made her look taller and the soft trim around the neckline flattered her skin.

"I just hope I won't be a wallflower."

I laughed. "Fat chance of that! You'll be the most popular girl there."

When we went downstairs, Dux whistled. "Wow! Chubby, you're a knockout! Nobody will ever believe you're my mother-in-law."

Upon arriving at the club, I led Mother to the powder room. While I was hanging up our coats in the entrance way and talking to friends, she slipped into the lounge. Out of the corner of my eye, I could see her standing in front of the long mirror, running her hands down over her hips, but she stopped as soon as she caught me watching her, embarrassed at my seeing her vanity.

Dux was waiting for us, and as the three of us entered the main room, someone called out, "Here comes Mrs. Baldwin!" Heads turned and I felt a surge of pride flow through me.

I introduced Mother to our group, some of whom she'd met before. Questions came fast, and she launched into a recital of her experiences, her eyes sparkling with animation.

"Oh, there's a special exercise for that," she was saying, and she blushed when she looked at the men. "You sit on the floor with your legs stretched out in front and then by swinging your arms back and forth, you 'walk' on your . . . er . . . posterior."

The men started laughing, and one of them said, "Boy, I'd like a picture of my wife dragging her fat fanny across the room."

Mother looked at him and said sarcastically, "Of course, it isn't easy. Why don't you try it? It might do you some good, too."

That brought a howl. Not only was this man overweight, but his figure bore a striking resemblance to that of Santa Claus.

The orchestra started playing one of our favorite songs, and Dux tapped me on the shoulder. "Come on, Shortie, let's dance."

As we were dancing throughout the evening, I tried to keep an eye on Mother. I caught a glimpse of her on the floor several times, but mostly she sat against the wall talking to groups of people. After a couple of hours I suddenly realized she was nowhere in sight, and excusing myself, I went to find her. I ran into Pris Williams in the powder room.

"Have you seen Mother?" I asked her.

She laughed. "I certainly have. Come on and I'll show you. She's doing something this town has needed for years."

I followed her to the glassed-in porch that was used only in warm weather. There was Mother with a coat thrown over her shoulders, swaying her hips and counting time. She was teaching three of our male friends how to do the "Samba."

WAIT GABRIEL WAIT

All at once it dawned on me why she hadn't danced much that evening. She knew all the latest dances, but we didn't. We were all out of step but Mother!

24

Garden Of Opportunity

Tulips and daffodils were starting to come up, and the crocus were already blooming—a welcome sight after such a cold, snowy winter. The weather had turned warm, and the glorious spring days made us long to pore over seed catalogs and work outdoors.

Dux had been awarded a contract to build a pipeline in Canada several months ago and expected to go to Calgary within a few weeks. The ground for Mother's garden at Sandy Cove had already been plowed, and I knew she was thinking about going up north, but I wasn't sure when we'd be able to leave. As a dutiful wife, I always insisted on packing Dux's suitcase and driving him to the airport.

With characteristic energy, Mother had already plunged into her new project. Martha had set up two card tables near a window in the basement and covered them with old newspapers for protection. After a careful search through our garage and those of our neighbors, Mother had rounded up ten old flats and six large flower pots. Painstakingly sifting the peat moss, humus and black dirt, she spent hours preparing the soil and methodically planting and labeling each container.

Mother watched over her indoor garden as carefully as she'd watched over the incubator chicks. Only on the days we rolled bandages at the Red Cross could she be persuaded to leave the basement. When the first sprouts popped up, she shouted for everyone to come down and see the miracle. For as long as she had planted seeds, their germination had always been magic to her.

Dux left for Canada right after Decoration Day. By then, Mother was on pins and needles, and I promised her we'd go to the cottage the next day.

Loading the car to suit our persnickety gardener was almost impossible. She kept urging Martha and me to be careful how we handled the tender plants and continually changed her ideas on where to put them. First, they'd be better off in the trunk . . . no, set them on the back seat . . . no, well, maybe on the floor, or . . .

"Mother, make up your mind!" I said impatiently. "We've got two hundred miles to drive, and we want to be there before dark."

At last our suitcases, bedclothes and two boxes of canned goods went into the trunk, and we had to push with all our strength to lock it. Seven flats and four of the flower pots were on the back seat and floor while Mother sat sideways in front with the other plants under her feet.

We got to the lake late that afternoon, and it was good to get out of the crowded car. Although she didn't complain, I'm sure Mother's legs must have been cramped.

Sandy Cove looked more inviting than I'd remembered, and I was thrilled to be back again. Closing my eyes and taking a deep breath, I drank in the fresh air with its fragrant pine scent and listened to the gentle lapping of the water against the shore.

"Winalee, look what Jeff has done!" Mother's shout from the other side of Dux's tool shed interrupted my blissful tranquility. "Doesn't this soil look black and rich?"

Since the weather was a bit cool, Mother suggested that we leave the plants in the car until morning when Jeff would come over to help set them in the ground.

After we finished the endless transplanting the next day, Mother ran into the house and came back with several packets of vegetable and flower seeds. I groaned at the thought of more work, but she insisted and Jeff said he'd stay on and help us. Finally the last seed was planted and we both collapsed from exhaustion.

Mother was as proud as a peacock about her garden and worked in it almost every day. Although I helped her as much as possible, we still couldn't keep it under control. It was huge, much more than we needed. Mother called it her "victory triumph," but if we hadn't hired Jeff to keep it cultivated, the victory would have gone to the weeds.

Dux had to fly to Jackson on business three weeks later and was able to spend the weekend with us before returning to Canada. He loved to come to Sandy Cove as much as I did, and being away from it for such long periods was one of the sacrifices the construction business forced him to make.

Dux and I were sitting alone in front of the

fireplace talking and thoroughly enjoying the peaceful atmosphere of a quiet Saturday evening.

"Is something bothering Chubby?" he asked later as he was tamping the tobacco in his pipe. "She went to bed so early."

"I don't think so, honey," I answered with a complete lack of concern. "She never listens to the soap operas anymore and seldom crochets, but spends most of her time in the garden and seems to love it. I think she just wanted to leave us alone."

"Well, that's thoughtful of her." He got up to throw another log on the glowing embers. The nights were always a bit cool in northern Michigan, and we relished the warmth of the fire. He stood for a moment looking at the crackling blaze and then turned to me. "You know, Shortie, I've been wondering if Chubby would be willing to work—I mean, take a job with a salary."

"Oh, Dux, she'd jump at the chance!" I exclaimed. So many women were working these days, but then, what was Mother equipped to do? Her schooling had been mostly reading, writing, spelling and arithmetic, with accents on music, painting and the art of being a lady. In her day, marriage was the aim of all females, and that didn't require much intellectual knowledge.

"I could use her on the pipeline," he said. "Do you suppose she'd mind going back with me?"

"Mind? Oh, Dux, she'd love it!" A picture of Mother in coveralls and goggles flashed through my mind and I chuckled. But it really wasn't so fantastic. Since the war began, many women had taken over men's occupations; even sheltered ones were learning trades and doing jobs they'd never thought possible. Of course, Mother couldn't be a welder, but she wouldn't be afraid to tackle anything within reason.

Dux was saying, "This would be office work. When your dad was superintendent of the gas company's eastern division, Chubby made all his progress charts, kept his expenses and did other details he didn't like to do." He stopped a moment to relight his pipe. "I figured she could keep time cards, do payrolls and send me daily reports. Men are hard to get right now, and Frank Morris, my spread man, could bring her the information each night. There'd be no problem because they'd both be living in the Palliser Hotel." He turned to me for approval. "Well, what do you think?"

"Oh, honey, that's marvelous!" I gasped. "It would give her an income and make her feel independent. Golly, can we tell her now?"

He nodded and I hurried to her room and called out, "Mother, come quickly!"

Her door burst open and she rushed out, tying her robe around her. "What in the world has happened?"

I grabbed her, propelled her to a chair in the living room and pushed her into it. "Now you listen to your son-in-law. He wants to proposition you."

Her eyes brightened with eagerness as he told her about his idea. After asking several questions, she leaned back in the chair.

"Oh, it sounds wonderful! I can hardly believe it. Only Dux . . ." She stopped and a look of concern appeared on her face. "Do you really think I'm capable of doing this job justice?" she asked. "It's been such a long time . . ."

"Yes, I do," he assured her. "If I didn't think you could, I wouldn't be offering it to you. But you've got to understand one thing, Chubby—it's important work, and you may be there quite a long time."

"Oh, that wouldn't matter," she said quickly. Then thinking of me, she added, "Oh, Winalee, I didn't mean . . . of course, I'll miss you, but to be honestly useful and make money . . . oh, boy!" She clapped her hands in delight at the thought of it.

"Mother, I know exactly how you feel. It sounds

just right for you." I was sitting on the arm of Dux's chair and he reached for my hand. I could feel his fingers close warmly around mine.

For the next hour, they talked about the job, but never once did Mother ask about her salary. I think she would have been willing to work for any amount, and the prospect of living in an elegant hotel intrigued her.

Finally Dux decided we should go to bed. There'd be a lot to do tomorrow, and we had to go to Jackson the day after. Mother stood up, shook her head and looked at us.

"I'm simply flabbergasted! To think I'm going to have a real job!" She walked over to Dux. "I certainly hope you won't be disappointed in me."

He smiled and hugged her. "I know you can do it, Chubby. You've got what it takes."

All the way back to Jackson, Mother gave me directions about her garden. She was so keyed up that she didn't even realize how many times she repeated herself, but some of her advice came as a complete surprise to me.

"Don't let Jeff forget to put cheesecloth over the lettuce beds to keep them from going to seed. When you wash the green onions, don't let the tops get wet—they'll spoil quicker that way."

"You're remarkable." I laughed. "It's too bad you won't be here to enjoy the fruits of your labor."

"Well, 'you can't have your cake and eat it, too,' and I'm tickled pink that I can help Dux. Tonight I'll write Russell and tell him his old ma has a job on the pipeline. I know he'll be interested in that. I'm so thankful he and Bud are still in the States, but won't it be a red letter day when this dreadful war comes to an end."

"Amen to that!"

After we got home, Martha and I helped her get her clothes packed, and in the morning I drove Dux and Mother to the airport. Blinking back the tears, I kissed them good-bye. I kept thinking of the lonesome days ahead with both of them gone, but Mother was in her glory, and I felt a sense of elation that she was so happy. We'd had our ups and downs, but in the last year our relationship had become something special.

25

Luxurious Labor

"Winalee, I need some underwear. I
can't get the kind I wear up here in
Calgary, so when you go back to
Jackson, have Jacobson's send me
two braseres . . . no . . . brais . . . no
. . . oh, I can't spell it. I just looked
in my little dictionary, and all I can
find is brazier, a thing for holding
hot charcoal. Anyway, you know
what I mean, the things you got me
to start wearing a couple of years
ago."

I broke out laughing and flopped into a chair,
unable to control myself after reading this latest letter
from Mother. I could hardly wait to share it with
Ginger when she returned from the bus station in

West Branch.

Shortly before lunch, I heard a car door slam and saw Ginger walking toward the house with a good-looking Navy lieutenant.

"Mom, this is Bill Himburg." There was a lilt in her voice. "Doesn't he look handsome in his new uniform?"

Before I could say anything, Bill grabbed my hand. "Ginger has told me so much about you. I feel as though we've already met."

"We're so happy you could come," I said. "Ginger's been counting the days until you'd get here."

After Bill devoured three bacon, lettuce and tomato sandwiches, two glasses of milk and several brownies, they left and I went back to work. Mother's Victory Garden had flourished; in fact, it almost overwhelmed us. For me, at least, it had helped gain a victory over boredom, and with all the canning and freezing, I seldom had time to miss Mother and Dux. Even after taking baskets of vegetables to the West Branch Hospital, there were still enough left to give Jeff and the other neighbors all they wanted.

As I was scraping the carrots, Jeff came in to tell me the office had called Webster's store and that Dux would be arriving unexpectedly on Friday evening. I was so ecstatic over Jeff's news, I felt like throwing my arms around him and kissing him. How wonderful to have Dux home again!

When Dux's plane landed in the late afternoon, Ginger, Bill and I gave him a royal welcome. Bill offered to drive home, and Dux and I sat in the back seat holding hands and laughing, overjoyed at being together again.

Dux ate heartily at dinner that night, savoring every bite of our fresh vegetables after weeks of hotel

177

cooking. Our conversation naturally turned to Mother, and Ginger told Bill about some of her hilarious escapades.

"You'll be surprised when you meet my grandmother." She laughed. "You'll never guess her age."

"Since Mother lost weight," I said, "she honestly does look younger, and now that she is employed full time, she says she feels like a new person." I passed the green beans to Bill and wished Mother were here to enjoy them with us. How happy she would be to see the delicious bounty her garden was producing!

"So many construction workers have enlisted or been drafted," Dux explained to Bill, "that I honestly needed someone who could understand the work. Chubby's doing even better than I had expected," he said as he helped himself to some more sliced tomatoes, "but I just wish she wouldn't try to run the whole business. Frank, my spread man, says she keeps telling him other things that ought to be done, and once she even asked him to get a job for the husband of some waitress."

"That's typical of Mam-ma!" Ginger commented, looking at Bill.

"She sounds just like my grandmother," he said. "Gram's in her eighties, and when I went to see her last week she was up in a tree, sawing off a limb that was bothering her garden."

That tickled me. "Those two would really have a lot in common," I said to him. "Mother doesn't let her age restrict her either. There are several men she keeps writing about in every letter, and I've been wondering if they're all beaux."

"Could be, Shortie," Dux said with a playful glint in his eye. "Don't ever underestimate our Chubby!"

Later on, the four of us played bridge until I felt Ginger would want to be alone with Bill, so we excused ourselves and went to our room.

Monday morning came before I was ready for it. We'd all had such a good time together.

"I like Bill," I told Dux when I drove him to the airport, "and I've got a hunch those two could be serious, but as Mother would say, 'time will tell.'" I smiled to myself thinking of the way we all talked in hackneyed phrases since Mother had come to live with us. Dux often remarked that old maxims came up in our conversations like granite outcroppings in a field.

Ginger returned to Bennington the middle of September, and when Dux came home for a week in October, he took me back with him. This was my first trip to Calgary, and besides looking forward to being with Mother, I was eager to see the Canadian Rockies I'd heard so much about.

When we met Mother in the Palliser Hotel lobby, she greeted us with bear hugs. Mother and I were so excited we forgot we were in a public place, and Dux had to remind us to lower our voices.

"Mother, you look simply magnificent!" I told her in a loud whisper after we'd settled down to being ladies in a dignified atmosphere.

"Well, I just love it here, Winalee. I've made so many new friends, and I want you to meet all of them," she said, her eyes sparkling with vitality.

The next day while Mother and Dux were working, I went down to the dining room for lunch and was cornered by Miss Broop, a retired teacher whom I had met in the elevator. She was a sweet, fragile woman who hardly seemed to belong to Mother's generation. It wasn't merely that she looked older, but she seemed otherworldly in contrast with Mother's earthy bounce.

"Your mother is amazing," she said to me. "How old is she? We've all been trying to guess."

I laughed. "She's younger than I am in many ways, but age is merely a number, don't you agree? It hasn't anything to do with the way you think or the way you feel."

And that was true. Mother remained young in the things that counted—always looking forward, interested in today and expecting good for tomorrow. Her years didn't show, especially when she smiled.

That evening Mother took me to the office, and I met the night manager, a delightful red-haired gentleman with a fascinating Irish brogue. Afterwards we went into the lobby to visit, and every few minutes she would introduce me to another one of her friends. Most of them were retired and few seemed to like it. One man had been a salesman, but was now rather silent, apparently lost in memories and indifferent to the present. Another man read the daily papers closely, but I felt it was only so he could complain about the war and the way it was being run. He kept saying his war was the big one, and I actually believe he resented having another one.

"Reckon I must seem a bit flighty to these Canadians," Mother concluded after telling us about her life here. "They're so reserved. Oh, I forgot to tell you, last month we drove over to Banff and spent Saturday night at Lake Louise. I've never seen anything as beautiful as that blue-green water with the snow-capped mountains . . ."

"We?" I interrupted her. "Mother, who else went with you?"

She blushed. "Oh, that's right. You haven't met Alvin Crocker yet, but you'll see him tomorrow. I've invited him to have dinner with us. We play lots of cards together and almost every weekend we've gone dancing or on short trips somewhere. Of course, there were always others with us," she added quickly. "I'd never stay overnight just with him, but he's really a nice man."

The next evening when Alvin came for dinner, it was raining, and Mother decided we should eat in the hotel. Besides, that way we could meet her favorite waitress, Marie.

Alvin was a roly-poly man with snow-white hair complimenting his heart-shaped face and rosy cheeks. After I got acquainted with him, I decided he was sort of funny, in a vaguely effeminate way, but his manners were above reproach. He seemed to be a perfect gentleman and was always catering to Mother.

The night before Dux and I were to go home, Alvin took Dux out on the porch and started talking about Mother.

"I'm completely smitten," he said shyly. "I want your approval of me as her husband, if you agree . . ."

"Fine," Dux interrupted, "that is, if you can support her. She's darned expensive!"

Finally Alvin said in a choked voice. "Doesn't she . . . I mean . . . isn't she . . . independent?"

"As a hog on ice—but I'm the guy who keeps her that way," Dux told him. "When she marries, she's on her own, and I expect her husband to support her."

Dux and I left the next morning, and Alvin was the only one of Mother's friends who wasn't in the lobby to say good-bye. I noticed the apprehensive expression on her face.

Not long after we arrived home, we received a letter from her.

> "Dux, I want to know what you said to Alvin when I saw you two talking on the porch. He has avoided me ever since. I just don't understand. He told me he liked me, but he's dropped me like a hot potato. Please let me know what happened."

26

The Belle Of Fort Myers

When Mother came home a few days before Thanksgiving, she brought me up to date on all her friends in Calgary. That evening she launched into a full scale campaign of letter writing. Her prospective pen pals ranged from Marie, her favorite waitress, to the Irish night manager and included nine or ten retired women and men we met at the hotel.

Although none of the children could be here for the holiday, Martha went all out in fixing a delicious turkey dinner. Her special chestnut dressing, candied yams, succotash, cranberry salad and hot biscuits with honey were fit for a king. I noticed that Mother still watched what she ate and only had black coffee for dessert while Dux and I enjoyed our ample servings of plum pudding.

"Winalee, do you remember meeting a Mrs.

MacIntyre?" Mother asked me later as the two of us were sitting in the living room. Dux had gone upstairs to the bedroom to listen to the football game, or so he said.

"Vaguely," I answered lazily, having eaten too much turkey.

"Well, Rose MacIntyre is a lovely person, but quite a 'fraidy-cat.' She's at her home in Florida now and has been there by herself for three weeks, but she just hates being alone." Mother came over and sat down on the arm of my chair. "You know, Winalee, she wants me to come to Fort Myers."

"When?" Her surprising news roused me out of a state of semi-consciousness and I turned toward her.

"Right away," Mother answered enthusiastically. "I got a letter from her yesterday, and she said her cousins are coming for a visit the first of February, but she wants me to be with her until then."

"You mean before Christmas?" I could hardly believe my ears. Mother had only been home a short while and now she was ready to go again. What had happened to the old lady who used to hibernate in her room, listening to soap operas and crocheting, just waiting for Gabriel to blow his horn?

"Well, not if you and Dux want me to be here for the holidays," she said, and I sensed she realized how empty this year's Christmas would be without our boys. "Anyway, I have to find out if Dux will need me on the pipeline." She moved over and sat down on the foot stool in front of my chair.

"Dux doesn't do much pipelining in the wintertime, but do you think you know this MacIntyre woman well enough to stay such a long time with her?" It would be nice for Mother to be away from our long, cold winter, but I wondered if she'd be happy spending the holidays with strangers. Christmas had always been a "family time" for us, and I wouldn't want her to be lonely and unhappy away from her relatives.

"Oh, yes! We had a grand time together in Calgary. Rose was going with a friend of Alvin's while he was dating me. Don't you remember? I told you we all went to Banff together. That was the time she first mentioned my coming to Florida."

"Well, it's up to you, Mother. If you want to go, it's all right with me." I tried not to sound too disappointed, but I'd really been looking forward to her being with us again, at least for a while. Then, too, I knew Ginger would miss seeing her as she hadn't been with Mother since early last summer.

"Come on, Winalee." She jumped up, grabbed my hands and pulled me quickly off the chair. "Let's go upstairs and talk to Dux. I've got a snapshot of Rose's house in my purse I want to show you. It's a cute bungalow with lots of flowers and shrubs, and it even has a magnolia tree in the front yard." Her voice gathered enthusiasm with every step we took.

"What are you two girls making so much racket about?" Dux called from the bedroom in a drowsy voice.

"Oh, Dux, you're awake." Mother hurried down the hall. "There's something I want to tell you."

I followed her to our room in order not to miss a word.

Excitedly she told him all about her intended plans. He agreed with me that it was an excellent idea for her to go, and even suggested she find a place to live after the first of February if she liked the town well enough to stay the rest of the winter. There wouldn't be any pipeline work until spring, he assured her.

Mother called Mrs. MacIntyre the next evening to tell her that she would be coming on Sunday and gave her the flight schedule.

Getting ready for the holidays kept me busy until the time Ginger came home. She'd been in the house only a few hours when she announced her shocking intentions.

"I want to quit school and join the WAVES," she said seriously.

"Oh, no!" I gasped. "You can't. You're not old enough." I turned to Dux, my voice quivering, "You tell her . . ."

Dux cleared his throat. "I can understand your feeling of patriotism, dear, but I believe you have to be twenty before . . ."

"That's right, Dad," Ginger broke in, "but I'll be twenty in two months, and you and Mom will have to sign my application."

Dux stood up and put his hand on her shoulder. "We do want you to finish college, Ginger."

"Sweetheart, you're too young and your schooling is so important. It would break my heart for you to stop before you graduate." I knew I sounded like a typical mother, but I could hardly bear the thought of Ginger's enlisting in the Navy.

"But, Mom, it isn't fair to Bud, Russ and all the other boys. We're all in this war, and we've got to do everything we can."

"Let it go for now," Dux said, trying to appease the situation. "You get the forms, Ginger, and send them to us. When the time comes, we'll discuss it again." He leaned down and kissed her cheek.

Long after Dux had fallen asleep that night, I tossed and turned in my bed, my mind chaotic. There was no security anywhere. We all had to make sacrifices, and I could understand Ginger's wanting to help, but I never dreamed she'd be thinking she could do a man's job. I wished for more of Mother's fortitude, more of her courage to adjust to unexpected situations. I'd read somewhere that the current generations were becoming weaker, and I was ready to believe it.

Christmas came and went, and I missed Mother even more than I had expected, but the cheerfulness of her frequent letters indicated she loved Fort Myers. Dux and I suspected she would probably be staying there until spring.

"I've met so many nice people," she told us in a letter, "especially one man who's an excellent dancer. I've joined a group, and believe it or not, we play cards several evenings a week, but I still won't play for money."

"Well, what do you think of that?" I asked Dux.

"Poor Chubby," he said, "she's still wrestling with her conscience!"

Around the middle of January, Mother sent us an air mail special.

> "There's a woman down here who owns The Kopper Kettle Inn, and she's been trying to get someone to sublet the place so she can take a trip. She talked to me, but I told her I'd have to think about it, and I'd like to get your ideas. It's practically filled with people right now who have leases to the end of the season. I wouldn't have to serve meals. It would just mean being there and keeping the house clean, but that's no problem because there's a good cleaning woman. It's almost time for Rose's relatives to get here, so I'll either have to take this place or come home. Let me know what you think right away."

Dux laughed. "She can get into the darndest things—never satisfied to let well enough alone, but at least she's learned to ask our advice before she gets herself involved. You write her to find out the rent, the expenses, how much the tenants pay, how long the lease would be and to let us know.

The result was that Mother moved into The Kopper Kettle Inn early in February. In her first letter after becoming a landlady, she wrote about one of her roomers who was an author.

"I've never been so shocked in all my life," she had written. "Clara (my cleaning woman) and I read the typed pages this man throws away, and they're positively awful."

"Oh, Winalee," she told us later, "we always look forward to the day we clean his room and can get at his wastebasket to find out what happens next."

Dux and I chuckled every time we read one of her letters. We never knew what to expect! She was beginning to sound more interested in her dancing partner, and we wondered if he would turn out to be another Alvin—or if one day we'd get a letter saying she had eloped.

When Mother wrote saying she would definitely be home the first of May, I started counting the days. In anticipation of her arrival, Martha and I planned her favorite dinner and even got fresh flowers for the table since none of our bulbs had started to bloom.

"Oh, I had a perfectly marvelous time," she exclaimed when Dux and I met her at the airport. "The owner said I could have The Kopper Kettle Inn next year and that she'd send the lease for me to sign."

Mother was slightly tanned and looked a generation younger than anyone I knew around her age. Managing the Inn apparently hadn't been too strenuous for her. On the way home, we all sat in the front seat, and she kept us entertained with interesting stories about things that had happened and the histories of most of her house guests except the one who really intrigued us.

"Mr. Duvois didn't talk much to us, so it was hard for me to find out anything about him. I hope he sells that novel he's writing, but I simply can't imagine anyone paying money to read a book like that. It's all about those naughty streetwalkers in Paris. I'm certainly glad our government doesn't allow that sort of thing to go on in this country," she said emphatically.

"Is that so, Chubby?" Dux turned to me and winked. "Sounds like you've gotten a real education from that wastepaper basket!" he teased as he slowed down for a traffic light. "Now, tell us about your special dancing partner. What's he like?"

Mother smiled and blushed. "Oh, you mean E. J.?" she asked nonchalantly. "It seems funny to be interested in men at my age, but it certainly keeps life from being dull."

"Come on, Chubby," Dux said, starting to accelerate. "Stop procrastinating and tell us more about this guy."

"Well, his name is Ellsworth James Henry, but we all call him 'E.J.' for short. He's really a perfect gentleman. Next month he's coming to Detroit to visit his sister and he wants to see me, so I've invited him up to Sandy Cove to spend a few days. That's all right, isn't it?"

"Of course, Mother. Now that we have two new bedrooms, we'll love having company," I said, grateful that she felt free enough to have her friends come and stay with us.

"I'm anxious to see those new rooms. I couldn't tell much from your letter about the way they were built on. You know . . ." She hesitated and looked at me earnestly, and I wondered what was coming next. "Winalee . . . this man . . . I mean, E.J. . . . has asked me to marry him." There was an impish grin on her face.

"What'd you say?" I blurted out in sudden shock.

"For one thing, I want you two to look him over, but . . ." She looked down at her hands in her lap. "Getting married again . . . oh, I don't know."

Dux laughed. "Chubby, you're a hard gal to figure out! It seems to me you have everything just the way you like it right now. Why in the world would you want to get married?"

"Do you think you'd be happier, Mother?"

"Well, I'm not sure. I reckon most of the men who want to remarry are either looking for a nurse or a pile of money," she said. Then her eyes lit up. "That reminds me, I never did tell you what happened when I went home with Mrs. Simpson to meet her brother. Remember I told you about John—he was that lawyer

189

who was older than I am. Well, he was so money hungry, even his firm had to force him to retire." She was talking faster and getting madder by the minute. "Anyway, the night before I left he came right out and asked about my financial status. Said he might like to marry me if I had enough. I was thunderstruck! When I got my wits back, I told John it was none of his business, and I wouldn't marry him on a bet. For a while I was too humiliated to even tell you."

"That's awful!" I stated emphatically. "I wondered why you didn't want to talk about it."

I remembered that night when Mother came home from Washington and marveled at her ability to accept the challenges of the many unexpected opportunities that had come to her this year. She had adjusted so easily to them. My, how much her thinking had changed since coming to live with us!

27

Dangerous Woman

"It's long distance for you, Miz Baldwin," Martha reported, and Mother eagerly got up from the table and ran to the phone.

"That was E.J.," she announced excitedly when she returned. He called from Knoxville where he's visiting a nephew and said he'll be here around eight o'clock tomorrow night. I told him we'd meet him at the bus station."

"I'm glad he's coming," I said, "but we won't be able to pick him up. Don't you remember, Dux and I are flying to the lake this afternoon." E.J. hadn't wasted much time, I thought. It had only been a little over a month since Mother had seen him in Florida, and now he was coming to visit her.

"Oh, shoot! Now what'll I do? I'd hate to have him go to a hotel."

"Why can't he stay here?" I asked, puzzled at her remark. "There's plenty of room, and he can get a cab at the bus station."

She gasped. "I thought you told Martha she could have the rest of the week off, and we can't be here alone without a chaperone."

"Oh, for Pete's sake, Mother! Why not? Aren't you both old enough to behave yourselves?"

"But what will the neighbors think?"

"Just like I do. Anyway, what earthly difference does that make?"

"Reckon not any." She drew a deep breath. "But I never spent a night alone with a strange man in my whole life."

Dux and I got a big kick out of Mother being so jittery. In most ways, she had become quite modern, but I was surprised at how old-fashioned she could still be at times.

As we told her good-bye, Dux grinned and said, "Now remember, Chubby, be sure to behave yourself!"

Her face flushed and she replied playfully, "Maybe you shouldn't trust me so much!"

Two days later I met the bus in West Branch and brought Mother and E.J. to Sandy Cove. E.J. was nice-looking and had kept himself in excellent condition. Instantly I felt a sense of honesty and sincerity when I looked into his clear hazel eyes.

After Dux had taken E.J. down to the dock and we were alone, I noticed that Mother kept chuckling to herself, so I asked her what was so funny.

"Well, Winalee, don't you dare tell this to anyone, but this morning I awoke early, made coffee and took a cup upstairs to E.J.'s room, you know—like you do for Dux." She kept giggling. "I knocked on the door and called out, 'It's time to get up, E.J. I'll scoot this coffee in for you,' and don't you know . . ." She couldn't continue, she was laughing so hard. Finally she said, "When I turned the knob, the door was locked!"

I began laughing with her. "Mother, that's a scream! He must have been afraid of your immoral advances."

"Well, at first, I was sort of mad. I just left the cup at his door and ran downstairs. Then I saw the joke was really on me, and I couldn't wait to tell you."

We liked E.J. a great deal. Although he was somewhat shy, he had a keen sense of humor, and it was very easy to talk to him. Dux and he had many interesting discussions, but I noticed when Mother came into the room, he'd jump to his feet, seeming to forget about everything else.

When we were washing the dinner dishes, I said to her, "I can tell that E.J.'s really in love with you. What are you going to do?"

Mother shook her head. "I do enjoy being with him. He's a lot of fun, but I don't know about marriage. Maybe I like my independence too well, and at my age . . ."

"You're a lot younger than anyone I know, Mother. Age is really a point of view, as you've always said, and it hasn't anything to do with the years you've been through."

My mother was the living proof of this statement, and I wondered why she had to be reminded of it every so often. Normally, age was not a part of her thought or conversation. Never would she tell anyone how old she was, and she'd made me promise I wouldn't either.

"Well, I'll tell you, Winalee, E.J. is ten years younger than I am, but he doesn't know it, and I'm certainly not going to tell him."

I snickered. "Mother, you're a real Jezebel!"

As E.J. was leaving, Mother encouraged him to come back any time he could. They walked out to the car hand in hand like two young lovers, and he kissed her good-bye as though he really meant it.

The summer days flew quickly. Mother and I were busy working at the West Branch Red Cross several mornings a week, adding the finishing touches to the new bedrooms and weeding the garden. It was not as large as last year, but still required a lot of time. Many evenings we invited neighbors over to play cards, and Mother seemed contented and satisfied even though there wasn't anything special for her to do.

Dux was able to be with us more often than last summer since most of his pipeline work now was in Ohio. Whenever he could, he'd fly up for the weekend and I always loved our time together.

Each day Mother looked forward to the mail delivery and was seldom disappointed. E.J. was a faithful correspondent and, judging by the length of his letters, he must have kept her well-informed. When she told me he had changed his plans and was going to stay in Detroit with his sister for the next few months, I wasn't sure that his decision was made entirely because of Florida's sultry summer weather.

"Winalee, would it be all right if I invited E.J. to spend next weekend with us?" Mother asked expectantly one afternoon late in July.

"It'd be fine with us, Mother. We haven't made any plans, but I thought you were flying back to Jackson with Dux on Monday."

"Oh, that would still be all right." She had already figured things out. "He said he'd be back here Friday afternoon."

"Wonderful!" I smiled at Mother's anticipation.

"We'd love to have him."

I met E.J.'s bus on Friday before Mother and Dux had come. Later, as we were having a pleasant visit in the living room, I heard the plane. Dux would always circle the cottage as a signal to let me know when to pick him up. As we ran outside to wave, we were astonished to see the plane go into a dive. For a moment, my heart stopped beating. Then Dux pulled out of it and began doing lazy eights and a series of barrel rolls. Finally he headed toward the landing field, and E.J. and I jumped into the car to meet them.

I was furious all the way to the airport, thinking how petrified Mother must have been.

"I don't know what ever got into Dux," I told E.J. "He's usually so careful not to frighten anyone."

"Well, sometimes even the best of us make errors in judgment," he said, trying to help Dux get out of the dog house. But it would take more than that for me to forgive him.

As we pulled up to the airport gate, we could see Mother and Dux calmly waiting for us.

"For heaven's sake, Dux," I sputtered angrily after we'd greeted each other. "What on earth . . ."

"Now you stop, Winalee," Mother said. "I asked him to do those tricks. I was hoping E.J. would see us." A sudden flicker of embarrassment crossed her face.

"But weren't you scared, Hattie?" E.J. asked admiringly.

"Not really. It did seem funny when I opened my eyes and saw the lake where the sky ought to be, but with Dux at the controls, I didn't worry. Besides, I like a little danger once in a while," she added flippantly.

My anger melted into amusement as I looked at E.J. He was staring at Mother in wide-eyed wonder, like a lovesick cow! Is there really such a thing as perennial youth?   Watching Mother and E.J. almost convinced me there was.

28

The Forbidden Gown

Last February Dux and I had signed Ginger's application to join the WAVES. After several phone calls, letters and an investigation of this newly-formed organization, we decided it was the right thing to do. Although we really hated to have her leave Bennington, her patriotism finally won out. Boot training had been at Hunter College in New York City, and she was now working as a radio operator in Washington, D.C.

Our sacrifices were small in comparison with those that other families were making. The war had surely changed everyone's lives, but at least we knew our boys were all right: Bud was still an instructor at Camp Hulen in Texas, and Russ had been shipped to some place in southern England.

The telephone rang one night early in October,

197

and Mother hurried to answer it.

"It's Ginger," she called out.

"Hi, sweetheart!" I said. "How's everything going?"

"Okay, I guess. Bill left a few days ago and he's shipping out soon." She paused. "I'm so blue . . ." Her voice broke, and she sounded ready to cry. "Oh, Mom, how do you know when you're in love?"

Before I could answer, Mother cut in from the upstairs extension. "You just know, Ginger. When it happens, you won't have any doubts. You'll think a ton of bricks has fallen on you," she said without hesitation, and her voice sounded as if she spoke from experience.

"Mam-ma's right, honey," I said, trying to cheer her up. "You'll know for sure, and it won't be the uniform or the war. Your heart will just tell you."

"Oh, Mom!" She broke into sobs. "I'm miserable. Do you suppose either of you could come to Washington? I'm so lonesome without Bill. During the day, of course, I'm busy, but the evenings are horrible. I really do need my family."

"I don't see why we both can't come," Mother immediately decided for the two of us. "I bet we can get a plane out of here tomorrow."

"We'll talk about it, honey, and I'll call you back later. Keep your chin up, dear, and remember, we all love you," I said, just before I hung up the phone.

Mother and I talked about Ginger until Dux got home. After discussing the situation with him, we called her back to say we would be coming the day after tomorrow.

When we got to the hotel, Ginger was there waiting. Rooms were very hard to find during the war, but Dux had called a business associate who was able to reserve one for us.

"Oh, sweetheart, you look darling in your uniform," I said, standing back and looking at her.

"She sure does," Mother agreed. "You'd look good in anything, though, it's been so long since I've seen you."

"I know it, Mam-ma. You're a real gadabout! I can hardly keep up with you," Ginger teased her lovingly. "Boy, you don't know what it means to have you here."

After standing in line to register for over fifteen minutes, the clerk told us it would be some time before our room would be ready. When she heard this, Mother excused herself to find the ladies' room.

"This delay is typical of Washington. It's a real mad house around here," Ginger told me. "Everyone is trying to cut through some form of red tape, and the whole place is a bureaucratic mess."

"Hey, you two," Mother said on her return. "There's a nice elderly gentleman over there who offered me his key. Wouldn't it be a good idea to sort of freshen up in his room before dinner since we can't get into ours?"

"Shame on you, Mam-ma," Ginger scolded, "don't you know what he's after? He thought you were by yourself. He's just looking for a pick-up."

Mother threw up her hands in shock, exclaiming, "Land o' mercy! Ginger, are you sure? I just can't believe it." She looked cautiously over her shoulder. "Let's get out of here right now." As we left the lobby, Mother's eyes were glued straight in front of her.

At dinner that night, Ginger talked mostly about Bill: his good manners, the way his eyes shone, the difficult job he had, his nice family and the fact that we all lived in Michigan. Both Mother and I sensed that she was really in love, whether she knew it or not.

Ginger was free the next day and we decided to go shopping. There were men and women in uniforms wherever we looked. The loud cries of the newsboys on each corner could be heard above the noise of the traffic. Since Mussolini had been ousted and the Italians were now helping us fight Germany, the war news was beginning to look optimistic.

As we crossed the street to go to Garfinckel's, Ginger pointed out a lovely lace wedding dress in their window.

"I wanted to try it on," she said, "but they wouldn't let me. They told me they couldn't take it out of their display."

Mother looked puzzled. "What do you mean? Don't they want to sell it?"

"Sure they do, Mam-ma," Ginger told her, "but they don't consider the WAVES as 'shoppers.' They think we're just 'lookers,' and I guess maybe that's true. Why should we buy anything new when we have to wear our uniforms all the time?"

"I'll fix that," I told them, and we entered the store, with Ginger leading the way to the bridal salon.

"My daughter would like to try on the lace wedding gown that's in the window," I stated. The tone of my voice dared the bridal consultant to refuse my request.

"Certainly," she said politely. "Make yourselves comfortable, and I'll have someone get it for you."

As we sat down, we all looked at each other with a knowing smile. I decided in advance that if this was what Ginger wanted and it fit her, I'd go ahead and buy it, even though I didn't know when she'd need it. Remembering how much time I spent trying to find Lee's dress, I didn't want that to happen again.

"You look perfectly beautiful," we told Ginger when she came out of the fitting room wearing the dress.

"Oh, Mom, I just adore it! It's everything I've ever dreamed of," she said ecstatically. "Don't you love the way it fits?" Twirling around in front of us, she began humming "Here Comes the Bride."

We spent the rest of the week in Washington, and the day before we left, Ginger confessed, "You know those bricks you mentioned, Mam-ma, well, I've decided they've fallen, and they're crushing me down." Her eyes filled. "But I can't say I'm happy. I just feel awful."

Mother put her arms around her. "That's because you aren't with Bill, honey. Love should make you feel wonderful," she told her sympathetically, "that is, when you're together."

Ah ha, I thought, are you saying this merely to console Ginger, or is this your feeling about Ellsworth James Henry, too? I only wish I knew.

29

Harriet's Last Request

Living with Mother had taught me so much. I used to think her happiness and well-being were my responsibility, but now I had learned that we were both equally capable and that our separate personalities could blend together to help each other. Mother had made a world for herself in which she was comfortable and satisfied. It had taken time and hadn't been easy for any of us, but looking back, I saw it had been worth every agonizing step.

We'd had such fun together on our Washington trip that I hated to have her leave for Florida so soon. However, she had signed the lease again for The Kopper Kettle Inn and needed to get it ready for the winter season.

After spending several days carefully packing her summer clothes, Mother left, eager to get back to the warm sunshine. Four days later, I was overjoyed to find her first letter waiting for me when I returned from an overnight business trip with Dux.

Mother wrote that the weather had not been favorable, and she was worried about the tourist trade. Most of her guests had returned with the exception of Mr. Duvois. His "indecent" book had been published, and she'd seen a copy in the local bookstore. Dux and I wondered what she'd do for entertainment without his crumpled waste paper, but, with E.J. so constantly mentioned in her letters, we knew he must be spending a lot of time there.

Shortly after the new year, an emergency call came from E.J. in Fort Myers. Mother had been hit by a truck while crossing a street and was scheduled for surgery the next morning. I told him we'd be on the first plane out of Detroit.

I frantically called Dux at the office, and we were able to make flight reservations for early that evening.

E.J. was there to meet us when we got off the plane. Seeing his kind face, full of strength and compassion, helped to quiet my anxious thoughts.

"Hattie says to tell you not to worry," he told me when Dux went to get our luggage. "Your mother is a remarkable woman, Winalee."

"Yes, that's true." Tears filled my eyes. "She's come through so much. This couldn't possibly be the end." I opened my bag to get a handkerchief.

"Don't worry, dear, she's going to be all right." He put his arm around me. "You'd better get a good night's sleep—you'll have to be brave tomorrow, for Hattie's sake."

It was cold and rainy the next morning, and the gloomy weather didn't help our gnawing fears. We arrived at the hospital early, and although E.J. told us everything he knew, Dux still asked to speak with the doctor to get first-hand information. The nurse took me to Mother's room.

"Is that you, Winalee?" she called weakly. "Oh, it's so good to see you. Did Dux come with you?"

"Yes, Mother." I leaned over to kiss her. "He's in talking with the doctor now. E.J. is here, too."

"Oh, Winalee, isn't he sweet!" She smiled faintly and reached over to touch my hand.

"Yes, dear, and he's been so helpful to us, too," I said. "We all know you're going to be all right," I assured her, but looking at the strained, white face before me, I didn't feel as confident as my words sounded.

I waited while the interns lifted Mother onto the cart, and as they rolled her down the hall, I walked along beside them, holding her hand. Just before we came to the double doors, she gently tugged on my sleeve. I bent over her tenderly, fully realizing this could be our last moment together.

"If I die," she whispered groggily, "don't you dare put my age in the obituary!"

Utterly amazed, I kissed her, smiling through my tears. What a marvelous sense of humor she has, even at a time like this, I thought gratefully.

They took her into surgery and I hurried to find Dux. Meeting him at the elevator, I burst into tears.

"Don't worry, Shortie," he said, taking me in his arms. He led me toward the waiting room. "Dr. Grant said she has acute abdominal injuries, but that even though this is usually serious for a woman of her age, she has a good chance of recovery. Her positive outlook is especially in her favor." He took out his handkerchief and wiped my eyes. "Come on, Sweet, she'll come out of this as good as new," he reassured me. "Let's go down and have a bite to eat."

E.J. had been waiting anxiously in the main floor lounge, and we invited him to have breakfast with us. Even though we couldn't eat much, it did help to pass the time. When we went back upstairs, Dr. Grant was just coming out of the operating room.

"She's going to be fine," he reported confidently. "She came through with flying colors. You can go home now and have a good rest."

I had a dozen questions I wanted to ask, but hearing his name being called over the intercom, I decided not to detain him. Our prayers had truly been answered and gratitude overwhelmed me. Old Gabriel had been much too close to suit me, but Mother outsmarted him.

Two weeks later, Dr. Grant gave Mother permission to go home. Since Dux had gone back to Jackson the day after the operation, E. J. again offered his services and drove me to the hospital to get her.

"That's my daughter. I'd know her step anywhere," I heard Mother say as I approached her door. She was sitting on the edge of the bed, ready to leave, and the nurse was wrapping some of her newer bouquets of flowers to take home.

Looking bright and eager, Mother greeted me warmly. "I thought this day would never get here," she said excitedly.

Ten minutes later, a young orderly arrived with her wheelchair.

"Hi, there, Elmer!" Mother said. "How's your father feeling?"

"Much better, thank you, Mrs. Baldwin," he answered as he helped her into the chair. "When we heard Dr. Grant was releasing you today, we all spoke of how much we'd miss you." He placed a blanket over her knees and started rolling her out the door.

"I'll miss all of you, too," Mother told him, waving good-bye to the patients as she was wheeled down the hall. "But I'll come back and see everyone just as soon as I can," she promised.

E. J. and I tucked Mother into the back seat of the car amidst flowers and get-well presents.

As soon as he started the engine, I turned around and faced her. "Mother," I began, "I want you to listen to me. I have something special to tell you. After your operation and Dux was back home, I had quite a time trying to manage the tourist business and get new tenants." Just the thought of it now made me weary. I heaved a sigh and added, "I don't see how you ever did it. Anyway, during the middle of our last rainy spell, two more of your roomers left. They said Florida had never had such miserable weather and they were going back home. It was then I decided a drastic step needed to be taken."

"Oh, Winalee!" she gasped, "What did you do?"

"Wait a minute, Mother. I'm not finished. Because of this long cold spell, there are lots of vacant apartments, and I found one I'm sure you'll like."

"What on earth . . ." She was wringing her hands.

I interrupted her again, and continuing on, I told her the various steps I'd taken, from getting her out of the lease to moving all her things into her new apartment. "The owner said she'd give you first choice on the The Kopper Kettle Inn for next winter if you want it." I took a deep breath. "So now, we're on our way to your new home." Leaning back against the seat, I took a deep breath and relaxed. "Okay, it's your turn to talk."

"Gee whiz! I'm simply thunderstruck! I don't know what to say."

"Well, I do," E. J. put in. "Hattie dear, I think Winalee's absolutely right. I'm so relieved you don't have all that responsibility after such a serious operation, and besides," his voice softened, "now we'll have more time to go places."

Mother's whole expression changed, and a coy look

came across her face. "Well, now that you put it that way, I reckon it's for the best. Actually, I didn't want to tell you, but Dr. Grant did say I should take it easy for awhile." Suddenly her face clouded. "The only thing is," she added, "I won't be earning a cent, and I'll be costing Dux more money."

Smiling to myself, I decided not to tell her how much cheaper it would be for us if she'd stop trying to support herself!

30

Matrimonial Pandemonium

"That old ton of bricks certainly has fallen," Mother said. She'd been in Jackson only a few days and was looking marvelous, fully recovered from her surgery. "Now where do we start? It's been so long since I was married, I can hardly remember what to do first."

My thoughts were a jumble and I sat down to think while Mother waited impatiently. Let's see, the fireplace would make a good altar with a few candles and flowers from the florist. To make enough room for the guests, we'll have to move out all of the furniture—I could probably get Mr. Wickett to take it to the garage. Martha, bless her heart, would take charge of everything in the food department and maybe get her sister to help. Pris Williams has a fancy cloth I could borrow for the table, no, Mother finally finished my crocheted one and it would be absolutely perfect. Surely our neighbors will want to help—several of them are in my garden club, and I know their yards are full of beautiful flowers they could use to make arrangements for the house.

I mentally went on this way for several minutes planning all the details. Then somewhat organized and eager to get started, I turned to Mother. "Okay, you start making a list of the people you think we should invite. I'll call Lee and Jim, order the cake, make arrangements with the florist and get in touch with the minister. When I'm through with the phone, you can start calling your friends."

How perfect it would be if all the family could be here! It was such a shame the boys wouldn't be able to come for this important occasion. Russ had been in the invasion of Normandy on D-day and was somewhere in France. Bud was expected to be shipped out momentarily, and it was impossible for him to get leave.

By the time Ginger arrived with her two friends on Friday afternoon, practically everything was ready.

"Sweetheart, I hope we haven't let you down," I said as I gave her a big hug.

It had only been two days since she had called from Washington, putting us all into a mad whirl.

"Oh, Mom!" she had said breathlessly. "Bill just called and he's in California." She was so thrilled she could hardly talk. "His ship is in for repairs, and it might take a month, and . . . Mom . . . we want to get married!"

"Wonderful, darling!" I exclaimed. "How soon?"

"This Saturday! Oh, I'm too excited to even think straight."

"Saturday?" I couldn't believe I'd heard right. "Do

you realize today is Wednesday? I can't possibly . . ."

Mother, listening in on the extension as usual when Ginger called, broke in, "Honey, I'm so happy for you. Now don't you worry. I'll help your mother, and even if it isn't up to snuff, at least it'll be legal."

"Mam-ma, you're a jewel! What about it, Mom?"

"Well," I said, gradually coming out of shock, "if you think it can be done, we'll try."

We continued talking for the next fifteen minutes, and all three of us enthusiastically contributed ideas for the forthcoming event.

Ginger took the girls upstairs while Mother and I followed and filled them in on our preparations.

"Oh, Mom, you'll never know how much I appreciate this. I can hardly believe it, and to think Bill will be here in a few minutes!"

What a change in Ginger's outlook since last fall in Washington! It was wonderful to see her joyous and so obviously in love.

The rehearsal that evening was utter bedlam. Afterwards, we had cake and coffee in the kitchen and laughed over the many mistakes we'd made. Rehearsals were always chaotic, it seemed to me, but I'd never seen a wedding that wasn't beautiful and I knew Ginger's would go smoothly tomorrow.

The bright sunshine pouring in our windows awakened me the next morning. I bounced out of bed, delighted at the good weather and anticipating a happy day. When I went downstairs, Martha was serving breakfast in shifts.

Bill's parents came soon after we'd finished eating, and I quickly decided they would make excellent in-laws for my daughter. Dux and I both liked Bill very much, so it was not surprising to me that his parents were such fine people.

Later, as I was getting dressed for the wedding, Lee burst into my bedroom, close to tears. "Mom, look!" She pulled her dress away from her body and said, "Ginger got this a size too big and just look at it! What'll I do?"

"Run to Mam-ma, honey," I confidently told her. "She's the one who knows how to fix things." I was sure Mother would think of something to solve the problem. How grateful I was that she was so capable! Afterwards I noticed that Mother had sewn her up, making a couple of small pleats that probably wouldn't be seen.

Just before the ceremony was to start, Ginger came out into the hall and everyone raved about her gorgeous dress.

"Ginger, you look even lovelier than I remembered," Mother exclaimed. "Reckon it's because you're so happy."

A few minutes later, Mother began to play the wedding march on the piano, and everyone in the living room looked toward the door. The two bridesmaids entered and took their places by the altar. Lee came in next. Walking at a snail's pace, little Jimmy, carefully carrying the gold wedding ring on the tiny pillow took his place beside Jim.

Then Ginger, on Dux's arm, gracefully walked down the aisle. Dux was so nervous he had a scowl on his face, and it made quite a contrast with Ginger's radiant smile. A low murmur spread throughout the room. It took all the strength I could muster to control my emotion; I didn't dare look at Dux.

When the minister asked for the ring, Jim reached down to take it off the pillow and little Jimmy piped out, "Don't take my ring, Daddy!" A sound of muffled laughter followed.

Suddenly it was all over. Ginger changed back into her uniform, and we watched them run to Bill's car amid showers of rice. Gay colored streamers, tin cans and a "Just Married" sign were flopping in the breeze as they slowly drove away.

"Well, honey, we did it." Mother squeezed my hand. "There were times when I didn't know just how well things would turn out," she confessed. "But, by golly, everyone I talked with was mighty impressed," she added with a proud smile.

"I was, too, Mother. Everything was just perfect!" Tears flooded my eyes as we walked back into the house.

31

The Wall Of Inspiration

Mother had spent a leisurely summer at Sandy
Cove, and with the exception of E.J., who came for
two visits, she hadn't seen any of her friends.
However, she kept in constant touch with them and
always knew what they were doing. I wondered if the
West Branch Post Office needed to hire extra help to
keep up with Mother's correspondence.

Full of her usual ambition, she had decided to
renew her lease on The Kopper Kettle Inn for the
coming season. She had written everyone in Fort
Myers, telling them when she would be returning, and
her fall calendar was already filling up with important
social engagements.

Since she was so eager to get away, we
encouraged her to leave early and stop by West
Liberty on her way to Florida. That was all she

213

needed, and she left right after Labor Day.

Her first few letters didn't sound like she was having too much fun, and we questioned if we'd made a mistake in suggesting that she go there.

"Listen to this," I said to Dux one evening. Unfolding Mother's latest letter, I began to read.

"That bare, white wall behind the baptismal fount just looks terrible. Nancy said they'd intended to put a painting on it, but they ran out of money. She thinks I ought to do a picture they could hang there. I haven't done anything like this in years, but I figure after I get to Florida, I'll have plenty of time. I've already spoken to the Reverend, and he said it was a wonderful idea. What do you and Dux think about it?"

"Should we tell her?" Dux grinned, and I knew he was thinking of her monstrous, dark efforts in our attic.

"Oh, Dux, don't you dare say a word!" I threatened. "You remember what I went through with your Dawson, don't you?"

"Well, at least it'll give her something to do, and it's bound to be less expensive than raising chickens."

Thanksgiving Day we called Mother in Fort Myers, and the new painting project was her main topic of conversation.

"You know, I just love the hours I spend in my studio room. I'd forgotten how much enjoyment my oils gave me. Oh, Winalee, I certainly hope it works out that Ginger can get a holiday leave and you can all come for Christmas. I'm anxious for you to see my painting."

The next few weeks flew by for me. Dux had been doing more and more business traveling, and I went with him most of the time. Ginger was able to get away, and we made plans to meet her in Florida.

Christmas Day at the The Kopper Kettle Inn fully measured up to our expectations. Mother had invited E. J. to be with us, and she outdid herself in preparing a delicious turkey dinner with all the trimmings. I wondered if her supreme efforts were for us or for E. J.'s benefit.

She could hardly wait until the dishes were finished to take us into the empty room that she used as her art studio. With great dignity, she unveiled the huge canvas.

"Well, folks, what do you think?" she asked eagerly, watching our faces. "Remember, I've only started, and I've still got a lot more work to do." She pointed out the figures of Jesus and John the Baptist.

"I didn't know you were so good, Mam-ma," Ginger raved, with surprise in her voice.

"Neither did I." The enthusiasm in Dux's voice amazed me, but I could understand why. "Your proportions look about right," he was saying as he stood back and analyzed her work.

I walked over and threw my arms around Mother. "Oh, it looks wonderful! That sky is such a heavenly blue, you'd almost think it was real."

"Oh, Winalee, do you think it'll be good enough?"

"Mother, to be perfectly honest with you, I'm absolutely dumbfounded. It's even better than I thought it would be, and you chose such bright and uplifting colors."

"You know, I'm just beginning to realize that my old pictures were much too dark," she commented, "but then, that's the way we were taught in those days." She clasped her hands together and said intensely, "Oh, how I want this to be worthy of the church."

"It will be, Hattie. Look how well you've done up to now," E.J. encouraged her. "Don't concern your pretty head about it."

"But I just can't do faces. I'm so worried about painting them when the time comes." She looked at us with a forlorn expression.

"Mam-ma," Ginger suggested, "did you ever think of going to the high school to find an art teacher to help you?"

"That's a good idea," Dux put in. "Why don't you try it, Chubby? There must be someone . . ."

"I know, dear," E.J. said and his eyes lit up. "My landlord's son is a portrait artist in Punta Gorda, and if he can't help you, I'll bet he knows another artist who could."

"That sounds wonderful, Mother."

"But Punta Gorda is so far away. I couldn't take this canvas on the bus," she said despairingly.

E.J. again came to the rescue. "You know, Hattie, I'm sure we could find a way to rope it on the top of my car. Why don't you let me see what I can work out?"

The rest of the day we played cards, mostly canasta and bolivia, until Dux and Ginger were so bored they almost fell asleep.

Fortunately, this time the weather was gorgeous, completely unlike the miserable cold rains which plagued us last January when Mother had the accident. Dux and Ginger went deep sea fishing twice, and almost every day we swam and had a picnic on the beach.

Our Christmas vacation had been especially satisfying this year. We had learned more about appreciating each other and were grateful for the family we had with us, as small as it was.

Ginger was back in Washington, and Dux and I

had been home almost a month when another letter from Mother arrived.

> "The artist E.J. found for me has been so helpful. I've already had several lessons and things are progressing nicely. I had the biggest problem getting the right expression in the Master's eyes, but now I think I've captured it. I'm going to write the minister tonight and ask him about the dedication ceremony. I think we should set the date now, so everyone can make plans."

As I finished reading her letter, there was a lump in my throat, and I knew how much this meant to her.

Early in March, an air mail letter arrived from Fort Myers.

> "The dedication is set for the first Sunday in May. E.J.'s been saving up his gas rationing coupons for a long time, so he could bring the picture and me to Kentucky. Bless his heart! Don't you know, he bought a bronze plate for me to put under the picture."

This was one time I knew we'd put our company second, and Dux and I would surely be there. We'd no doubt drive as Mother would be coming home with us, and I was glad we didn't have a problem getting gasoline coupons. Because of Dux's business traveling, he could get all we needed.

Kentucky in May was breathtaking. The weather had turned warm, and all the countryside was bursting with life.

Mother and E.J. met us at Aunt Nancy's on Thursday evening for a family reunion. What fun it was seeing all the relatives—many of them a lot slimmer than I remembered. I wondered how they managed to stay so thin with such good southern cooking.

The next day we took Mother's painting to the church for the first time, and Dux and E.J. held it against the wall. It was beyond our wildest expectations!

"Those faces are simply excellent," I gasped. "In fact, the whole painting is excellent," I corrected myself. "You must have been divinely inspired."

"No, it's not right." She frowned. "The canvas is too small. That cold, white plaster just ruins the effect."

"Hattie, I think it looks fine," E.J. said, trying to console her, "and I'm sure nobody will ever think about the size."

Dux, still supporting the heavy canvas on his knee, peered around to look at it. "E.J.'s right, Chubby. Don't worry about it. Your painting is as good as any you'd see in a museum, and the wall isn't important."

Mother's disappointment disturbed me, but I didn't see how we could change anything. She studied it for a moment, then looked at me, obviously having arrived at a solution.

"Winalee, go back and ask Nancy if Will Sawyer is still around," she ordered. "He's a carpenter and if he can come over I think we can fix it," she stated confidently.

Turning to Dux and E.J., she said, "You can set that down now, boys, we've got work to do."

Mother had a plan all worked out, and when we returned to the church in the late afternoon, we began to understand what she had in mind.

Mr. Sawyer had finished butting up sections of

beaverboard between the canvas and the wall and was preparing the surface for painting.

Saturday morning Dux and E.J. helped Mother climb the ladder and handed her the palette, oils and brushes. Taking turns holding the ladder steady, we watched her squirt green and blue paints on the palette and start mixing colors. There was a smile of contentment on her face. Soon blue skies and green trees began to appear on the beaverboard, and by early afternoon it was impossible to tell where the original canvas ended.

"Chubby, you're a genius!" Dux hugged her tired body.

"I always knowed she was, even way back when Mrs. Baldwin give music lessons to my little Nell," Mr. Sawyer said. He had been with us most of the day, fascinated by the transformation of his beaverboard.

"Thank you, Will," she said humbly. "I appreciate what you did." She turned to us with a triumphant smile. "I guess now it's ready."

Looking at Mother's satisfied expression, my face burned as I recalled the time Dan Rees hung Dux's Dawson and I'd angrily called her "just an amateur." Now, with great respect, I said, "Mother, you're a real artist!"

BAPTISM OF CHRIST
Painted and Presented to The Christian Church
by
Harriet Cole Baldwin
May 1945

32

Dedicated To Life

Sunday was a glorious day for the dedication ceremony. Mother was usually ready ahead of time, but today she was so jittery and excited about the occasion that she'd gotten up at the crack of dawn and sat patiently waiting for a full hour. All the pains-taking efforts she took in getting dressed were evident as she was absolutely stunning in her soft blue linen dress with matching shoes. The darling blue flowered hat added just the right touch. As I stood looking at her, an enormous sense of love and pride welled up within me.

There were only a few people at the church when we arrived and an usher took Mother's arm, escorting her to our special seats. E.J., Dux and I followed behind them. As we sat there waiting for the service to begin and admiring her finished masterpiece, we could hear the low whispers of approval all around us.

The minister began the ceremony with a brief sermon, and then he talked about Mother, giving a short history of her life in West Liberty, mentioning her many charitable activities and the courage she displayed in the face of her paralysis. I could hear the sound of pocketbooks opening and closing throughout the service as the minister's voice filled with increasing emotion. There probably wasn't a dry handkerchief left in the church when it was over and mine was no exception.

Coffee was served in the basement after the ceremony, and one by one the members came up to congratulate Mother. They talked of old times and laughed at many funny things that had happened over the years. Several women spoke of their struggles with Mother's reducing course and said West Liberty hadn't been the same since Mother moved to Michigan. Will Sawyer cornered Dux and E.J. for a full fifteen minutes before I was able to rescue them.

The next morning we were packed and almost ready to leave Aunt Nancy's when a neighbor came running in shouting, "The war is over! It's all over! Germany's given up! We've won!"

At last, Germany had surrendered. With tears of joy running down our cheeks, we all started hugging and kissing each other and literally jumped up and down. We had known things were getting better for the past few weeks, but hadn't imagined it would be over so quickly. It was hard to believe—and to think Russ and Bud would be back soon. In fact, all our boys would be coming home and I was so happy for everyone. Then I thought of Ginger and knew how especially thankful she'd be, for it wouldn't take much more time to end the Pacific battle. I wished President Roosevelt had lived long enough to see this day.

"Did E.J. mind going back to Fort Myers alone?" I asked Mother as we were on our way driving back to Jackson.

"No," she answered. "He's got another sister in Atlanta, and he's planning to visit her for awhile."

Dux reached across my lap to turn on the radio. "It's time for the news," he announced. "You girls keep still for a few minutes."

Seconds later, we heard the voice of the newscaster describing the peace settlement with Germany. While he was speaking, my mind wandered back to the inspiring dedication. What a rich experience it had been for all of us! Mother seemed happier than I ever remembered her. Giving so unselfishly of herself to help her church, she alone had received the greatest blessing. I felt such great admiration for her, and I knew everyone else had benefited by her example. All at once I realized how much we would have forfeited had she not come to live with us.

The music was now playing over the radio, so I reached forward and switched it off. "Is E.J. planning to come to Sandy Cove this summer?" I continued as if there had been no interruption.

"I guess so," she hedged. "We spoke about it." Suddenly Mother turned toward me. "Winalee, I forgot to tell you. I talked to a man in Florida about a brand new business that sounds fascinating, and he ships hundreds of boxes all over the country."

Hardly paying any attention, I said, "I want to hear all about it, but first tell me . . ." Pausing for a moment to find the right words, I asked, "Do you and E.J. have any . . . other future plans?"

"Well, nothing really definite," she answered evasively. "I did tell him, though, that I wanted to go to Alaska to see Drexel."

"Chubby, what's in those boxes you mentioned?" Dux asked suspiciously. He was probably wondering if his tool shed was in danger of invasion again.

"Oh, Dux, it's a marvelous idea!" she replied enthusiastically. "There's a good profit in it with so many fishermen, especially around the lake, and they're grown in barrels sunken in the ground." Her excitement had been mounting, but suddenly she stopped and a perplexed look crossed her face. "One thing bothers me though . . . how can I find out about the sex life of a worm?"